Personal
TRAINING
& WORKOUT
diary

HINKLER
BOOKS

First published in 2009
by Hinkler Books Pty Ltd
45–55 Fairchild Street
Heatherton Victoria 3202 Australia
www.hinklerbooks.com

© Hinkler Books Pty Ltd 2009

Prepress by Graphic Print Group

2 4 6 8 10 9 7 5 3
10 12 14 13 11

ISBN 978 1 7418 3077 4

Printed and bound in China

It is recommended that you check with your doctor or healthcare professional before
commencing any exercise regime. While every care has been taken in the preparation of
this material, the publishers and their respective employees or agents will not accept
responsibility for injury or damage occasioned to any person as a result of participation in
the activities described in this book.

INTRODUCTION

How often have you said, 'I need to exercise', but not followed through? Have you started an exercise program only to stop within weeks? When starting a training program, most people's intentions aren't to stop after a short while. Unfortunately, this is often exactly what happens. It would be great to be fit and healthy with no effort, but it can take a lot of hard work to achieve your fitness and weight loss goals.

A personal training diary can help you reach those goals. Recording training sessions and food intake makes you more aware of what you put in your body and how you burn it off. This information can help you set goals and targets, plan exercise sessions and learn what works for you.

Health, fitness and weight

While most people would like to keep slim and fit, there are also serious reasons for maintaining a healthy weight. The World Health Organization (WHO) estimates that at least one in three adults are overweight and one in 10 are obese. Even a slightly overweight person has a higher risk of health problems, which increases the more overweight a person is. Improving fitness and maintaining a healthy weight has many benefits, including:

- a reduction in the risk of heart disease, stroke, diabetes, osteoarthritis, cancer, skin problems, respiratory conditions, infertility, gallbladder disease and hypertension
- increased lean muscle, body tone, strength, endurance, cardiovascular fitness and energy levels
- increased core and joint stability, reducing related pain and injuries
- better recovery from injury and illness
- posture and flexibility improvements
- improved performance levels, greater self-confidence and better sleep patterns
- a stronger metabolism, increasing the rate the body burns fat.

While excess weight can cause health problems, it's also something that you can control. While your genes can influence weight, the most effective way to become lean is through a combination of strength and cardiovascular training. The other vital ingredient is a sensible, healthy eating plan.

Remember, if you are starting a new diet or exercise regime, have a check-up with your doctor first. By making changes to your diet and lifestyle, you'll reduce the risk of disease, feel happier, have more energy, sleep better, handle stress more effectively and look great!

Calculating BMI

The body mass index (BMI) measures whether someone is considered overweight. To obtain your BMI, use the following formula:

BMI = weight in kilograms divided by the square of height in meters

A woman who weighs 76kg and is 1.79m tall works out her BMI by dividing 76 by 3.2 (her height of 1.79 squared, or 1.79 x 1.79). 76 divided by 3.2 equals a BMI of 23.75.

The classifications used by the WHO are :

Classification	BMI
Underweight	< 18.50
Healthy range	18.50–24.99
Overweight	25.00–29.99
Obese	30.00–39.99
Morbidly obese	> 40.00

Body shape, build and ethnic origin affect BMI, so it is a guide only. People from an Asian background are classified as overweight if their BMI is more than 23 and people from a Pacific Islander background are classified as overweight if their BMI is more than 26. Do not use the BMI for children under 15 or the elderly.

The risks are greater if a person has excess fat around the abdomen. If your BMI is over 25 and your waist measures more than 101cm (40") for men and 88cm (35") for women, the risk of disease is greater than for a person who gains weight on other parts of their body, such as their hips and thighs.

Checking your waist–hip ratio can be a good way to assess your risk for heart disease, diabetes and some cancers. Measure your weight at its narrowest point and your hips at their widest. Divide your waist measurement by your hip measurement to get your ratio. Ideally, women should have a waist–hip ratio of 0.7 or less and men should have a waist–hip ratio of 0.9 or less.

Strength training

Strength or resistance training improves muscle and bone density, metabolic rate, muscle mass and endurance. This is important as you age, as older people's muscles lose strength. Strength or resistance training includes free weights, training machines, exercising with bands or tubes, and calisthenics (such as sit-ups, push-ups and pull-ups).

Try to complete two or three sessions a week of resistance or weight training of at least 20 minutes. The intensity and weight will vary depending on your strength and fitness levels. Have at least a day's break between sessions for muscles to recover.

Technique and breathing

Technique is important to reduce the risk of injury and get the most from a workout. Start at an easy level and ensure you have mastered the technique before progressing. A single repeat of a movement is a repetition and a group of repetitions is a set. Breathe as normally as possible. Exhale on the exertion part of the movement and inhale on the return movement. Generally allow around two minutes recovery time between sets of the same exercise or exercises of the same muscle group.

Load

Load is the resistance applied to each repetition. Increasing the weight, slowing a movement or changing position can increase a movement's load and intensity.

Training intensity

To increase strength, a gradual and progressive increase in workload is required. After a load increase, gradually increase repetitions to the set target and then increase the load again. To ensure your body is getting the best possible workout, take your muscles to a point they haven't previously been. This may mean working to muscle failure.

Cardio training

Cardiovascular training conditions the heart and lungs. It contributes to heart health, oxygen uptake and use, endurance, energy and fitness. Cardio training affects metabolism and the body's use of fat as an energy source.

Frequency

The WHO recommends moderate activity for at least 30 minutes a day. If you currently do no cardio training, a few times a week is appropriate in the early stages. Don't believe 'the more training, the better'. If you over-train, you won't achieve faster. On the contrary, you can end up sore, tired, bored, frustrated, injured and back where you started.

Length of cardio sessions

The length of each session depends on your fitness level and the intensity level that you exercise at. The more intense a session, the shorter it can be. Below is a list of cardiovascular sports and their recommended duration.

Walking	30–60 minutes
Jogging/running	15–40 minutes
Cycling	20–60 minutes
Swimming	20–40 minutes
Skipping	15–30 minutes
Stair walking or running	15–30 minutes
Aerobics or water aerobics class	45–60 minutes
Tennis, squash, golf, touch rugby, bowls, cricket, football, netball, basketball, softball, baseball, soccer	30–60 minutes
Boxing, martial arts, boxercise	30–60 minutes

Intensity of cardio sessions

Exercise at a level that enables your muscles to respond and adapt. If your level is too easy, you will only maintain your fitness level. However, don't push yourself too hard. Cardio exercise should make you breathe heavily and your heart beat faster. If you can easily talk, your intensity isn't high enough. If you can't talk at all, it's too high. If you can get words out between heavy breathing, then your intensity is appropriate.

Start at an easy-to-moderate intensity and gradually increase it. Moderate exercise includes brisk walking, light weight training, cycling and mowing the lawn. Increase cardiovascular intensity by going faster or longer or making the exercise more difficult.

Also try to have a few sessions of more vigorous exercise of least 30 minutes. It should make you sweat and puff so that talking is very hard. It includes jogging, fast swimming, exercise classes, squash, singles tennis, power walking, team sports and fast cycling.

Activity	Approx. kJ/cal burned per hour	Activity	Approx. kJ/cal burned per hour
Sleeping	230/55	Brisk walking	1750/420
Eating	355/85	Basketball	1750/420
Sitting	355/85	Aerobics	1885/450
Standing	420/100	Moderate cycling	1885/450
Driving	460/110	Jogging	2090/500
Housework	670/160	Digging	2090/500
Golf	1000/240	Fast swimming	2090/500
Calisthenics	1000/240	Cross trainer	2090/500
Slow cycling	1000/240	Hiking	2090/500
Slow walking	1000/240	Step class	2300/550
Gardening	1045/250	Rowing	2300/550
Ballroom dancing	1090/260	Power walking	2510/600
Walking	1170/280	Heavy weight training	2510/600
Slow swimming	1250/300	Exercise bike or fast cycling	2720/650
Raking garden	1465/350		
Tennis (singles)	1465/350	Squash	2720/650
Rollerblading	1750/420	Skipping	2390/700
Vigorous dancing	1750/420	Running	2390/700

Stretching and flexibility

Stretching is an important part of exercise programs, yet it's often neglected. This can jeopardize a program's long-term effectiveness. Stretching two or three times a week makes your exercise more effective and your body more supple.

Regular stretching keeps you flexible and helps prevent muscle injury and soreness. It improves muscle elasticity by increasing blood flow to the muscles and helps lengthen and strengthen them. Never hold your breath as you stretch. Perform a range of long, slow stretches that target different muscles one by one.

The best time to stretch is after training, as the muscles are already warm and more pliable and can be moved into positions where a long-term benefit can result. Each stretch needs to be performed correctly: technique is a priority to ensure full effect and to prevent injuries. Try the following stretches after a workout. Hold each stretch for 30–60 seconds.

Triceps stretch
Stand up straight. Lift both arms above your head and bend your elbows. Hold your right elbow with your left hand and push it down behind your back and hold. Repeat with the other arm.

Shoulder stretch
Place your left arm across your body, keeping it parallel to the ground. With your other hand, push in towards your chest and hold. Repeat with the other arm.

Lower-back stretch

Lie on your back. Pull one knee up to your chest until you feel a stretch. Hold your knee to your chest with your arms. Make sure the other leg remains flat on the ground. Hold and then repeat with the other leg.

Hip flexor stretch

Keeping the back straight, kneel forward on one knee. Place the other foot in front, keeping the bottom tucked under. Lean forward so that your weight is on the front leg. Hold and then repeat with the other leg.

Standing quadriceps stretch

Stand straight, using an object for support if necessary. Hold your ankle and pull your foot up behind until you feel a stretch. Hold and then repeat with the other leg.

Standing adductor stretch

Standing with feet apart, lunge sideways to the left, bending your knee and taking your weight on your left leg until you feel a stretch in your groin. Hold and then repeat to the other side.

Upper back stretch

Kneel on your hand and knees. Stretch your arms out in front as your head drops down towards the floor and your bottom moves back towards your heels until you feel a stretch. Hold.

Torso twist stretch

Sit on the floor with the right leg stretched out in front. Bend the left leg over the right knee. Place left arm behind you for support and the right arm outside the left knee. Rotate the left shoulder and hold. Repeat on the other side.

Seated adductor

Sit on the floor with knees bent and the soles of the feet together in front of you. As you relax your knees to the floor, pull your heels towards you until you feel a stretch in the groin and hold.

Abdominal and lower back stretch

Lie face down on the floor with your hands out in front, supporting your body weight. Straighten the elbows to raise the chest until you feel a stretch in your lower back and abdomen. Hold. If this is difficult, hold your arms further out in front.

Calf stretch

If necessary, lean against a wall or an object for support. Place your right foot in front of you with the knee bent and the left leg straight out behind. Keeping your left heel on the ground, lean forward until you feel a stretch. Hold, then repeat with the other leg.

Lumbar rotation stretch

Lie on your back with your legs together. Pull both legs up to the chest and then rotate them to one side, keeping your shoulders flat on the floor. Hold and then repeat on the other side.

Warming up and cooling down

Warming up before exercise involves slowly building up activity so that blood flow to the muscles increases and warms the tissues, the heart rate slowly increases and adrenalin is released to lubricate the joints. A warm-up should relate to the exercise that you're about to do. If you were going to exercise your legs, do some gentle jogging on the spot. Some easy stretches should also be performed. For strength training, perform one or two easy warm-up sets before commencing.

Cooling down can help delay and reduce muscle soreness and is done at a lower intensity than the exercise. It keeps the blood flowing through the muscles and prevents the build up of lactic acid and dizziness. Slowly reduce the rate of exercise for five to ten minutes and perform a series of stretches.

Setting goals and staying motivated

Achieving empowers and motivates you to keep improving. Goals should be realistic, challenging, specific and measureable, with a time frame and a plan for their completion. If necessary, talk to a fitness professional about what targets are appropriate.

Set challenging but achievable short, medium and long-term goals, as you'll lose motivation if you fail to reach your targets. For example, a short-term goal is to walk 5km in under 40 minutes in a month. A medium-term goal is to run 3km without stopping in three months. A long-term goal is to compete in an 8km fun run in six months.

Competing against yourself is a great way to get results. Try to beat your previous time or perform more repetitions. Look for handy gadgets such as pedometers, heart rate monitors and distance monitors to measure your performance.

It is easy to lose motivation if you try to achieve too much or if you do activities that you don't enjoy or that don't fit your lifestyle. Choose a variety of activities so you won't get bored or frustrated. Exercising with a friend or a trainer is a great way to keep motivated. There's no better motivation than reaching your goals and seeing the results!

Exercise and activity tips

- Be active every day. Look for ways to be active in your daily life and make exercise a regular part of your family and social life
- Regard exercise as a bonus, not a bother. Choose activities that you enjoy
- Join a gym or fitness club, get a personal trainer or play a team sport
- Work out with an exercise partner
- Set goals and try and beat them. Don't be unrealistic with your targets
- Train for an event or competition
- Use a training journal.

Nutrition

The main reason for eating is to provide the body with the energy it needs day to day. Many people skip meals or make bad choices when they need quality nutrition and energy. The problem gets worse when people eat the majority of their food in the evening, when they least need it.

A healthy diet

A good diet is made up of foods that are high in fiber and low in fat. A healthy diet focuses on a variety of foods that provide the body with the right amount of fuel and nutrition. Read the labels on food packaging to see what nutrients, fat content and energy the food contains. An up-to-date fat, fiber, kilojoule/calorie counter is a great help.

Daily, you should aim to eat at least:
- five serves of vegetables
- five serves of wholegrain cereal, bread, rice, pasta and noodles
- two serves of fruit
- two serves of low-fat milk, yogurt, cheese and other dairy foods
- one serve of legumes and nuts
- a liter and a half of fluid.

Try to eat lean meat and poultry only two or three times a week and fish at least once or twice a week. Drink plenty of water and fluids to avoid dehydration.

To maintain a healthy diet, avoid:
- Fat, especially saturated fats
- Sugar and sugary food and drinks
- Fatty cuts of meat and processed meats
- Salt
- Alcohol (limit to one per day for women and two per day for men).

Drink coffee, tea and fruit juice in moderation, as coffee and tea contain caffeine and juice contains kilojoules/calories.

Healthy dieting tips

- Reduce portion sizes. However, increase the number of red, green and yellow vegetable servings. Try adding an extra vegetable to your meals
- Eat smaller meals more regularly
- Plan your meals ahead of time. Prepare healthy snacks, such as fruit, nuts or whole meal crackers
- Read the labels on food products. Some 'low fat' foods are high in sugar or kilojoules/calories
- Don't boil vegetables for too long, as they lose their nutrients and flavor
- Use herbs and spices to flavor food instead of fatty sauces or salt
- Choose wholegrain cereals over white or processed cereals
- Eat lots of fiber to feel fuller. Always eat a high-fiber breakfast, such as bran, whole wheat or oat cereal
- Don't set unachievable weight-loss goals.

Diet, exercise, supplements and vitamins

A well-planned, healthy diet that meets all nutritional needs is important for sporting and athletic performance. Consult a doctor or a sports nutritionist for the best ways to combine exercise, training and diet for optimum performance and results.

Carbohydrates are the most effective source of energy, as they are broken down into glucose, which is used as an energy source by the muscles when you exercise. Nutritionists recommend that over than half of energy intake should come from carbohydrates. Athletes and strength trainers may need to increase that amount to two thirds of their energy intake. No more than a third of energy should come from fats and about 15 per cent from proteins.

Protein and amino acid supplements are popular with athletes and strength trainers. While athletes do require more protein in their diet, health professionals recommend this comes from a healthy diet. The recommended daily amount of protein for a regular, active person is 0.75 grams of protein per kilogram of body weight. For sportspeople, that can increase from 0.75 to 1 gram per kilogram and for high performance endurance athletes and strength trainers, that amount can increase to up to 1.7 grams of protein per kilogram.

Significantly higher protein intake can be harmful. Excess consumption of protein can lead to dehydration, kidney failure, less bone density and weight gain. Drink lots of water if you are on a high-protein diet and only take protein supplements (such as whey protein), bars and shakes if you are not getting enough protein in your daily diet.

A small amount of protein (such as a yogurt or a bowl of cereal) before and after you exercise can increase muscle development. After your workout, try to eat foods that combine protein and carbohydrates to optimize how muscles rebuild and repair. Avoid sugary foods and drinks.

A healthy diet should also contain an adequate amount of vitamins and minerals. Use vitamin supplements as directed and do not take higher than recommended doses, as some vitamins and minerals are toxic in larger amounts.

How to use the diary

This diary is designed as a complete record of your exercise sessions and results over twelve months. It is divided into days, weeks, months and a year so you can monitor exercise and dietary practices and behaviors. As the diary is not dated, you can start recording information at any time.

Twelve-month planner

The diary starts off with a twelve-month planner that allows you to record events over the course of a year. Use this section to fill in major events and occurrences that could affect your exercise sessions and dietary habits throughout the year.

Yearly assessments

Record your details at the start and end of the twelve-month period covered by the diary. Use the first assessment page at the beginning of your program to set out your measurements and targets. The end-of-year assessment lets you assess whether you've met or surpassed those goals.

Weekly records

The weekly record forms the major part of the diary. Set weekly targets, plan your calorie intake and record your weight, BMI and waist–hip ratio. There's also space to record lifestyle information.

The exercise diary lets you enter your strength and cardio training sessions throughout the week. Record the focus area, the equipment used, the number of sets and reps and the weight you've used in your strength training. Use the cardio training page to note information such as heart rate, exercise intensity and calories burnt.

Use the food diary to record your daily totals of fat and calories. Add up the totals to show your overall weekly food consumption and compare it against your goal from the start of the week.

Monthly evaluation

Use the monthly evaluation pages to set goals and measure your progress over the past month. Check your average daily calorie and fat consumption over the course of a month. By assessing your weight, fitness and body measurements at the start of the month and comparing it against your results at the end of the month, you'll not only have a great idea of your progress but also be motivated to keep up the good work!

Yearly heart rate graph

The heart rate graph is a great visual way to track your fitness over the course of twelve months. Each week, simply mark your resting and maximum heart rates on the graph. As the year progresses, you'll get a good idea of how you are doing with your program.

Personal bests

Record your best times and results in this section. Update the chart with your progress and new bests, and use this information to help set new goals and targets.

Start-of-Year Assessment

DATE 6 / 06 / 09   AGE 32   HEIGHT 170

Current Physical Measurements	
Weight	86 kg
BMI	28
Waist–hip ratio	8
Chest, relaxed	101
Chest, expanded	104
Waist	86
Stomach	98
Hips	107
Neck	40
Shoulders	144
Right upper arm, relaxed	51
Right upper arm, flexed	52
Left upper arm, relaxed	51.5
Left upper arm, flexed	52
Right forearm, relaxed	45
Right forearm, flexed	46
Left forearm, relaxed	45
Left forearm, flexed	46
Right upper thigh	76
Right lower thigh	72
Left upper thigh	76
Left lower thigh	71.5
Right calf	49
Left calf	49

Physical Measurement Targets	
Weight	75 kg
BMI	24
Waist–hip ratio	7
Chest, relaxed	95
Chest, expanded	97
Waist	74
Stomach	88
Hips	94
Neck	37
Shoulders	137
Right upper arm, relaxed	44
Right upper arm, flexed	45
Left upper arm, relaxed	44
Left upper arm, flexed	45
Right forearm, relaxed	40
Right forearm, flexed	41
Left forearm, relaxed	40
Left forearm, flexed	41
Right upper thigh	65
Right lower thigh	62
Left upper thigh	65
Left lower thigh	62
Right calf	44
Left calf	44

	Current		Target	
Time how long it takes to run 2km/1 mile.		25		15
Count how many push-ups you can do before you have to stop.	Current	9	Target	20
Count how many sit-ups you can do before you have to stop.	Current	11	Target	25
Count how many squats you can do before you have to stop.	Current	28	Target	35
Sit with legs out straight. Place a ruler on the floor with the center between your feet. Record how many cm/inches you stretch up to or beyond your feet.	Current distance [+/-]	-10	Target distance [+/-]	+5
Time you can balance on one foot: right leg / left leg	Current	30 secs / 42 secs	Target	1 min. / 1 min.

Cardiovascular Fitness Test

Use the same course each time. It should take about 12 minutes to complete the first test, regardless of whether you walk or run.

- Record your resting heart rate before warming up
- Complete the course as fast as you can, recording your working heart rate every 3 minutes
- Still standing, record your recovery heart rate when you finish and then 1, 2 and 3 minutes after you finish
- Record the time it took to finish the course.

Cardiovascular Fitness Test	Current	Target
Resting heart rate	74	70
Working heart rate: after 3 minutes	210	200
after 6 minutes	215	200
after 9 minutes	217	200
Recovery heart rate: at course completion	220	200
1 minute after completion	205	170
2 minutes after completion	150	125
3 minutes after completion	124	100
Completion time	25	15

Current Personal Summary

	1–5			1–5
Strength level	2	Energy level		3
Endurance level	1	Sleep quality		2
Satisfaction with fitness	1	Stress level		2
Satisfaction with weight	2	Mood level		2
Quality of diet	2			

Personal Goals

Improve my strength and endurance.

Develop my fitness levels.

Week Beginning
22 / 06 / 09

Planned exercise sessions this week

	Exercise	Completed [Y/N]
Monday	Gym	N
Tuesday	Tennis	N
Wednesday	Training run	N
Thursday	Gym	N
Friday	Legs at pool	N
Saturday	Gym	N
Sunday	Dance class	N

Strength Training

MONDAY

Focus area	Equipment	SET 1 Weight	SET 1 Reps	SET 2 Weight	SET 2 Reps	SET 3 Weight	SET 3 Reps	SET 4 Weight	SET 4 Reps
Biceps	Free weights	20	10	20	10				
Calves	Machine	30	5	30	5	30	5		
Shoulders	Machine	30	5	30	5	30	5		

TUESDAY

Focus area	Equipment	SET 1 Weight	SET 1 Reps	SET 2 Weight	SET 2 Reps	SET 3 Weight	SET 3 Reps	SET 4 Weight	SET 4 Reps

WEDNESDAY

Focus area	Equipment	SET 1 Weight	SET 1 Reps	SET 2 Weight	SET 2 Reps	SET 3 Weight	SET 3 Reps	SET 4 Weight	SET 4 Reps

THURSDAY

Focus area	Equipment	SET 1 Weight	SET 1 Reps	SET 2 Weight	SET 2 Reps	SET 3 Weight	SET 3 Reps	SET 4 Weight	SET 4 Reps
Stomach	Machine	10	4	10	4	10	4		
Quads	Machine	40	36	40	36	40	36		
Glutes	Machine	40	36	40	36	40	36		
Triceps	Free weights	40	35	40	35	40	35	40	3

FRIDAY

Focus area	Equipment	SET 1 Weight	SET 1 Reps	SET 2 Weight	SET 2 Reps	SET 3 Weight	SET 3 Reps	SET 4 Weight	SET 4 Reps

SATURDAY

Focus area	Equipment	SET 1 Weight	SET 1 Reps	SET 2 Weight	SET 2 Reps	SET 3 Weight	SET 3 Reps	SET 4 Weight	SET 4 Reps
Biceps	Free weights	20	10	20	10	20	10		
Quads	Machine	40	6	40	6				
Calves	Machine	30	5	30	5				
Triceps	Free weights	40	6	40	6				

SUNDAY

Focus area	Equipment	SET 1 Weight	SET 1 Reps	SET 2 Weight	SET 2 Reps	SET 3 Weight	SET 3 Reps	SET 4 Weight	SET 4 Reps

Cardio Training

MONDAY

Exercise	Time	Distance/resistance	Intensity	Heart rate	Ease	kJ/Cal expended
Treadmill	20 mins	4 kms	Hard	205	4/10	200
Stepper	10 mins	1.5 kms	Hard	200	3/10	75
Aerobics	1 hr		Hard	205	4/10	450
Weights	20 mins		Medium	180	3/10	200
					Total:	925

TUESDAY

Exercise	Time	Distance/resistance	Intensity	Heart rate	Ease	kJ/Cal expended
Walk at lunch	30 mins	2 km	Medium	180	7/10	180
					Total:	180

WEDNESDAY

Exercise	Time	Distance/resistance	Intensity	Heart rate	Ease	kJ/Cal expended
Training run	40 mins	6 kms	Medium	210	3/10	400
					Total:	400

THURSDAY

Exercise	Time	Distance/resistance	Intensity	Heart rate	Ease	kJ/Cal expended
Treadmill	20 mins	4 km	Hard	210	4/10	200
Stepper	15 mins	2km	Hard	205	3/10	75
Aerobics	1 hr		Hard	205	4/10	450
Weights	20 mins		Medium	180	5/10	200
					Total:	925

FRIDAY

Exercise	Time	Distance/resistance	Intensity	Heart rate	Ease	kJ/Cal expended
Swimming	1 hr	2 km	Medium	196	6/10	500
					Total:	500

SATURDAY

Exercise	Time	Distance/resistance	Intensity	Heart rate	Ease	kJ/Cal expended
Treadmill	20 mins	4 km	Hard	200	4/10	200
Rowing machine	20 mins	2 km	Hard	210	5/10	190
Step class	1 hr		Hard	210	5/10	550
Weights	20 mins		Hard	190	4/10	200
					Total:	940

SUNDAY

Exercise	Time	Distance/resistance	Intensity	Heart rate	Ease	kJ/Cal expended
Dance class	2 hrs		Medium	180	7/10	840
					Total:	840
					Weekly Total:	3585

Food Diary

MONDAY

Breakfast Time: 8 am/pm		kJ/Cal	Fat	Protein	Carbs
	Cereal	309	23	9	74
	Banana	105	0.4	13	27
	Half cup of skim milk	56	0.2	6	3
Lunch Time: 1 am/pm	Pizza pocket	263	8	16	32
Dinner Time: 7 am/pm	Sun-dried tomato frittata	567	24	28	53
	Grilled vegies	51	51	3	11
	Ice cream	180	12	6	39
Snacks:	Yoghurt, 2 chocolate biscuits, orange	360	15.7	12.5	76.4
Coffees/teas: 3	Fluid intake: 4 glasses Totals:	1911	49.3	81.8	312.7

TUESDAY

Breakfast Time: 7.30 am/pm		kJ/Cal	Fat	Protein	Carbs
	Cereal	309	23	9	74
	Half cup of skim milk	56	0.2	6	0.3
Lunch Time: 1 am/pm	Tuna pita	105	1.5	9	12
Dinner Time: 7.30 am/pm	Tomato risotto	175	24	5	33
	Strawberries	12	5.1	0.6	3.6
Snacks:	Banana, cheese crackers	441	8.8	21	59.6
Coffees/teas: 1	Fluid intake: 5 glasses Totals:	1098	15.3	31.7	182.5

WEDNESDAY

Breakfast Time: 7.45 am/pm		kJ/Cal	Fat	Protein	Carbs
	Scrambled eggs	362	24.4	21	16
Lunch Time: 12.30 am/pm	Vegetarian pizza	314	8	18	43
Dinner Time: 6.30 am/pm	Chicken stir-fry	175	4.4	27	6
Snacks:	Apple muffin, cheese roll, banana	507	12.1	14.3	89
Coffees/teas: 0	Fluid intake: 8 glasses Totals:	1358	48.9	80.3	154

THURSDAY

Breakfast Time: am/pm		kJ/Cal	Fat	Protein	Carbs
	Cereal	309	23	9	74
	Half cup of skim milk	56	0.2	6	0.3
Lunch Time: 1.30 am/pm	Mediterranean sub	430	10.5	22	72
Dinner Time: 6 am/pm	Pork and spinach stir-fry	227	13.9	21	5
	Ice cream	180	12	6	39
Snacks:	Banana, raisin toast, chocolate biscuit	677	25.4	12.5	106.8
Coffees/teas: 2	Fluid intake: 2 glasses Totals:	1929	52.5	102.2	276.1

FRIDAY

Breakfast Time: 8 am/pm		kJ/Cal	Fat	Protein	Carbs
	Pancakes	128	48	4	16
	Blueberry sauce	46	0.2	-	11
Lunch Time: 12.30 am/pm	Turkey wrap	428	13.4	22	59
Dinner Time: 7 am/pm	Spicy chicken	264	9.5	33	11
	Mediterranean vegies	67	4.3	1	6
Snacks:	Orange, diet jelly	75	0.2	2.4	20.6
Coffees/teas: 1	Fluid intake: 6 glasses Totals:	941	75.8	61.1	108.2

SATURDAY

Breakfast Time: am/pm		kJ/Cal	Fat	Protein	Carbs
Lunch Time: 1.30 am/pm	Vegie curry	268	5	11	48
	Banana	105	0.4	13	27
Dinner Time: 7.30 am/pm	Beef stroganoff	322	12	26	22
	Vegies	67	0.4	2.6	13.4
Snacks:	Banana smoothie, grapes, yoghurt	589	7.2	18.2	108.7
Coffees/teas: 2	Fluid intake: 6 glasses Totals:	1351	25	59.1	246.6

SUNDAY

Breakfast Time: 9.30 am/pm		kJ/Cal	Fat	Protein	Carbs
	Omelette	77	4.5	7	77
Lunch Time: 1.30 am/pm	Chicken pita	388	18.9	27	29
Dinner Time: 6.30 am/pm	Red capsicum pasta	384	6.2	14	72
Snacks:	Raisin toast, diet jelly	447	17.6	11.1	17.6
Coffees/teas: 0	Fluid intake: 7 glasses Totals:	1296	47.2	59.1	67.2

Units of alcohol this week: 2   Total alcohol kJ/Cal: 148

Vitamins and supplements: Multi vitamin

Weekly Totals	kJ/Cal	Fat	Protein	Carbs
	285	466	1529	10082

Weekly Personal Summary

Energy level: 3   Stress level: 4
Hours of sleep: 38   Sleep quality: 2
Mood: 3   Appetite: 4

kJ/Cal intake	
Planned kJ/Cal	8400
Actual kJ/Cal	10082
Difference [+/-]	+1682

Weight at start of week: 82.5
Weight at end of week: 83
BMI at start of week: 27
BMI at end of week: 27

Injuries or illnesses: Headache on Tuesday

Monthly Summary

MONTH 6   DATE 1 / 12 / 09   AGE 33   HEIGHT 170

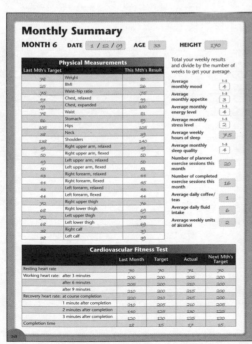

Physical Measurements

Last Mth's Target		This Mth's Result
78	Weight	80
25	BMI	26
.75	Waist–hip ratio	.75
97	Chest, relaxed	99
99	Chest, expanded	100
78	Waist	81
86	Stomach	89
105	Hips	105
38	Neck	39
138	Shoulders	140
49	Right upper arm, relaxed	49
50	Right upper arm, flexed	50
43	Left upper arm, relaxed	50
50	Left upper arm, flexed	51
43	Right forearm, relaxed	44
44	Right forearm, flexed	45
43	Left forearm, relaxed	43
44	Left forearm, flexed	44
72	Right upper thigh	76
68	Right lower thigh	69
72	Left upper thigh	75
68	Left lower thigh	69
38	Right calf	38
38	Left calf	39

Total your weekly results and divide by the number of weeks to get your average.

Average monthly mood (1–3)	4
Average monthly appetite (1–3)	3
Average monthly energy level (1–3)	4
Average monthly stress level (1–3)	2
Average weekly hours of sleep	7.5
Average monthly sleep quality (1–4)	4
Number of planned exercise sessions this month	20
Number of completed exercise sessions this month	16
Average daily coffee/teas	1
Average daily fluid intake	6
Average weekly units of alcohol	2

Cardiovascular Fitness Test

		Last Month	Target	Actual	Next Mth's Target
Resting heart rate:		70	70	71	70
Working heart rate:	after 3 minutes	200	200	205	200
	after 6 minutes	205	200	210	200
	after 9 minutes	210	210	215	210
Recovery heart rate:	at course completion	220	210	215	210
	1 minute after completion	210	205	210	205
	2 minutes after completion	140	125	130	125
	3 minutes after completion	120	120	125	120
Completion time		18	15	17	15

Endurance

	Last Month	Target	Actual	Next Mth's Target
Time to run 2km/1 mile	18	15	17	15
Number of push-ups before you have to stop	16	20	15	20
Number of sit-ups before you have to stop	20	25	25	25
Number of squats before you have to stop	230	35	32	35
Number of cm/inches you can stretch up to or beyond your feet (+/-)	0	+5	+2	+5
Time you can balance on one foot: right leg	35 secs	1 min	45 secs	1 min
left leg	32 secs	1 min	50 secs	1 min

Total your daily dietary results to get your monthly total.

Dietary Results

	Target	Result	Difference [+/-]
Fat intake	1150	1329	+179
kJ/Cal intake	28000	25030	+210
Carbs intake	6500	6410	-390
Protein intake	2000	1860	-140

Next Month's Targets

Physical Measurement Targets

	Next Mth's Target		Next Mth's Target
Weight		Left upper arm, relaxed	49
BMI	25	Left upper arm, flexed	50
Waist–hip ratio	.75	Right forearm, relaxed	44
Chest, relaxed	97	Right forearm, flexed	45
Chest, expanded	99	Left forearm, relaxed	44
Waist	76	Left forearm, flexed	45
Stomach		Right upper thigh	72
Hips	105	Right lower thigh	68
Neck	39	Left upper thigh	72
Shoulders	140	Left lower thigh	68
Right upper arm, relaxed	49	Right calf	38
Right upper arm, flexed	50	Left calf	38

Dietary Targets

	Next Mth's Target		Next Mth's Target
Fat	1150	Daily fluid intake	8
kJ/Cal	28000	Daily coffee/tea intake	2
Protein	2200	Weekly alcohol intake	1
Carbs	6400		

Twelve-Month Planner

	JANUARY	FEBRUARY	MARCH	APRIL	MAY	JUNE
1						
2						
3						
4						
5						
6						
7						
8						
9						
10						
11						
12						
13						
14						
15						
16						
17						
18						
19						
20						
21						
22						
23						
24						
25						
26						
27						
28						
29						
30						
31						
	JANUARY	FEBRUARY	MARCH	APRIL	MAY	JUNE

JULY	AUGUST	SEPTEMBER	OCTOBER	NOVEMBER	DECEMBER	
						6
						8
						9
						10
						11
						12
						13
						14
						15
						16
						17
						18
						19
						20
						21
						22
						23
						24
						25
						26
						27
						28
						29
						30
						31
JULY	AUGUST	SEPTEMBER	OCTOBER	NOVEMBER	DECEMBER	

Start-of-Year Assessment

DATE [/ /]   AGE [ ]   HEIGHT [ ]

Current Physical Measurements	
Weight	
BMI	
Waist–hip ratio	
Chest, relaxed	
Chest, expanded	
Waist	
Stomach	
Hips	
Neck	
Shoulders	
Right upper arm, relaxed	
Right upper arm, flexed	
Left upper arm, relaxed	
Left upper arm, flexed	
Right forearm, relaxed	
Right forearm, flexed	
Left forearm, relaxed	
Left forearm, flexed	
Right upper thigh	
Right lower thigh	
Left upper thigh	
Left lower thigh	
Right calf	
Left calf	

Physical Measurement Targets	
Weight	
BMI	
Waist–hip ratio	
Chest, relaxed	
Chest, expanded	
Waist	
Stomach	
Hips	
Neck	
Shoulders	
Right upper arm, relaxed	
Right upper arm, flexed	
Left upper arm, relaxed	
Left upper arm, flexed	
Right forearm, relaxed	
Right forearm, flexed	
Left forearm, relaxed	
Left forearm, flexed	
Right upper thigh	
Right lower thigh	
Left upper thigh	
Left lower thigh	
Right calf	
Left calf	

Time how long it takes to run 2km/1 mile.	Current		Target	
Count how many push-ups you can do before you have to stop.	Current		Target	
Count how many sit-ups you can do before you have to stop.	Current		Target	
Count how many squats you can do before you have to stop.	Current		Target	
Sit with legs out straight. Place a ruler on the floor with the center between your feet. Record how many cm/inches you stretch up to or beyond your feet.	Current distance [+/-]		Target distance [+/-]	
Time you can balance on one foot: right leg left leg	Current		Target	

Cardiovascular Fitness Test

Use the same course each time. It should take about 12 minutes to complete the first test, regardless of whether you walk or run.

- Record your resting heart rate before warming up
- Complete the course as fast as you can, recording your working heart rate every 3 minutes
- Still standing, record your recovery heart rate when you finish and then 1, 2 and 3 minutes after you finish
- Record the time it took to finish the course.

Cardiovascular Fitness Test		
	Current	Target
Resting heart rate		
Working heart rate: after 3 minutes		
after 6 minutes		
after 9 minutes		
Recovery heart rate: at course completion		
1 minute after completion		
2 minutes after completion		
3 minutes after completion		
Completion time		

Current Personal Summary

	1–5			1–5
Strength level	☐	Energy level		☐
Endurance level	☐	Sleep quality		☐
Satisfaction with fitness	☐	Stress level		☐
Satisfaction with weight	☐	Mood level		☐
Quality of diet	☐			

Personal Goals

_____

_____

_____

_____

_____

Week Beginning

[ ] / [ ] / [ ]

Planned exercise sessions this week

	Exercise	Completed [Y/N]
Monday		
Tuesday		
Wednesday		
Thursday		
Friday		
Saturday		
Sunday		

Strength Training

MONDAY

Focus area	Equipment	SET 1		SET 2		SET 3		SET 4	
		Weight	Reps	Weight	Reps	Weight	Reps	Weight	Reps

TUESDAY

Focus area	Equipment	SET 1		SET 2		SET 3		SET 4	
		Weight	Reps	Weight	Reps	Weight	Reps	Weight	Reps

WEDNESDAY

Focus area	Equipment	SET 1		SET 2		SET 3		SET 4	
		Weight	Reps	Weight	Reps	Weight	Reps	Weight	Reps

THURSDAY

Focus area	Equipment	SET 1		SET 2		SET 3		SET 4	
		Weight	Reps	Weight	Reps	Weight	Reps	Weight	Reps

FRIDAY

Focus area	Equipment	SET 1		SET 2		SET 3		SET 4	
		Weight	Reps	Weight	Reps	Weight	Reps	Weight	Reps

SATURDAY

Focus area	Equipment	SET 1		SET 2		SET 3		SET 4	
		Weight	Reps	Weight	Reps	Weight	Reps	Weight	Reps

SUNDAY

Focus area	Equipment	SET 1		SET 2		SET 3		SET 4	
		Weight	Reps	Weight	Reps	Weight	Reps	Weight	Reps

Cardio Training

MONDAY	Exercise	Time	Distance/resistance	Intensity	Heart rate	Ease	kJ/Cal expended
							Total:

TUESDAY	Exercise	Time	Distance/resistance	Intensity	Heart rate	Ease	kJ/Cal expended
							Total:

WEDNESDAY	Exercise	Time	Distance/resistance	Intensity	Heart rate	Ease	kJ/Cal expended
							Total:

THURSDAY	Exercise	Time	Distance/resistance	Intensity	Heart rate	Ease	kJ/Cal expended
							Total:

FRIDAY	Exercise	Time	Distance/resistance	Intensity	Heart rate	Ease	kJ/Cal expended
							Total:

SATURDAY	Exercise	Time	Distance/resistance	Intensity	Heart rate	Ease	kJ/Cal expended
							Total:

SUNDAY	Exercise	Time	Distance/resistance	Intensity	Heart rate	Ease	kJ/Cal expended
							Total:
							Weekly Total:

Food Diary

MONDAY		kJ/Cal	Fat	Protein	Carbs
Breakfast Time: am/pm					
Lunch Time: am/pm					
Dinner Time: am/pm					
Snacks:					
Coffees/teas:	**Fluid intake:**	**Totals:**			

TUESDAY		kJ/Cal	Fat	Protein	Carbs
Breakfast Time: am/pm					
Lunch Time: am/pm					
Dinner Time: am/pm					
Snacks:					
Coffees/teas:	**Fluid intake:**	**Totals:**			

WEDNESDAY		kJ/Cal	Fat	Protein	Carbs
Breakfast Time: am/pm					
Lunch Time: am/pm					
Dinner Time: am/pm					
Snacks:					
Coffees/teas:	**Fluid intake:**	**Totals:**			

THURSDAY		kJ/Cal	Fat	Protein	Carbs
Breakfast Time: am/pm					
Lunch Time: am/pm					
Dinner Time: am/pm					
Snacks:					
Coffees/teas:	**Fluid intake:**	**Totals:**			

FRIDAY			kJ/Cal	Fat	Protein	Carbs
Breakfast Time: am/pm						
Lunch Time: am/pm						
Dinner Time: am/pm						
Snacks:						
Coffees/teas:	Fluid intake:	Totals:				

SATURDAY			kJ/Cal	Fat	Protein	Carbs
Breakfast Time: am/pm						
Lunch Time: am/pm						
Dinner Time: am/pm						
Snacks:						
Coffees/teas:	Fluid intake:	Totals:				

SUNDAY			kJ/Cal	Fat	Protein	Carbs
Breakfast Time: am/pm						
Lunch Time: am/pm						
Dinner Time: am/pm						
Snacks:						
Coffees/teas:	Fluid intake:	Totals:				

Units of alcohol this week: [ ]   Total alcohol kJ/Cal: [ ]

Vitamins and supplements

Weekly Totals	kJ/Cal	Fat	Protein	Carbs

Weekly Personal Summary

Energy level [1–5]   Stress level [1–5]

Hours of sleep [ ]   Sleep quality [1–5]

Mood [1–5]   Appetite [1–5]

kJ/Cal intake

Planned kJ/Cal	
Actual kJ/Cal	
Difference [+/-]	

Weight at start of week [ ]

Weight at end of week [ ]

BMI at start of week [ ]

BMI at end of week [ ]

Injuries or illnesses [ ]

Week Beginning

[ ] / [ ] / [ ]

Planned exercise sessions this week

	Exercise	Completed [Y/N]
Monday		
Tuesday		
Wednesday		
Thursday		
Friday		
Saturday		
Sunday		

Strength Training

MONDAY

Focus area	Equipment	SET 1		SET 2		SET 3		SET 4	
		Weight	Reps	Weight	Reps	Weight	Reps	Weight	Reps

TUESDAY

Focus area	Equipment	SET 1		SET 2		SET 3		SET 4	
		Weight	Reps	Weight	Reps	Weight	Reps	Weight	Reps

WEDNESDAY

Focus area	Equipment	SET 1		SET 2		SET 3		SET 4	
		Weight	Reps	Weight	Reps	Weight	Reps	Weight	Reps

THURSDAY

Focus area	Equipment	SET 1		SET 2		SET 3		SET 4	
		Weight	Reps	Weight	Reps	Weight	Reps	Weight	Reps

FRIDAY

Focus area	Equipment	SET 1		SET 2		SET 3		SET 4	
		Weight	Reps	Weight	Reps	Weight	Reps	Weight	Reps

SATURDAY

Focus area	Equipment	SET 1		SET 2		SET 3		SET 4	
		Weight	Reps	Weight	Reps	Weight	Reps	Weight	Reps

SUNDAY

Focus area	Equipment	SET 1		SET 2		SET 3		SET 4	
		Weight	Reps	Weight	Reps	Weight	Reps	Weight	Reps

Cardio Training

	Exercise	Time	Distance/resistance	Intensity	Heart rate	Ease	kJ/Cal expended
MONDAY							
							Total:

	Exercise	Time	Distance/resistance	Intensity	Heart rate	Ease	kJ/Cal expended
TUESDAY							
							Total:

	Exercise	Time	Distance/resistance	Intensity	Heart rate	Ease	kJ/Cal expended
WEDNESDAY							
							Total:

	Exercise	Time	Distance/resistance	Intensity	Heart rate	Ease	kJ/Cal expended
THURSDAY							
							Total:

	Exercise	Time	Distance/resistance	Intensity	Heart rate	Ease	kJ/Cal expended
FRIDAY							
							Total:

	Exercise	Time	Distance/resistance	Intensity	Heart rate	Ease	kJ/Cal expended
SATURDAY							
							Total:

	Exercise	Time	Distance/resistance	Intensity	Heart rate	Ease	kJ/Cal expended
SUNDAY							
							Total:
							Weekly Total:

Food Diary

MONDAY		kJ/Cal	Fat	Protein	Carbs
Breakfast Time: am/pm					
Lunch Time: am/pm					
Dinner Time: am/pm					
Snacks:					
Coffees/teas:	Fluid intake:	Totals:			

TUESDAY		kJ/Cal	Fat	Protein	Carbs
Breakfast Time: am/pm					
Lunch Time: am/pm					
Dinner Time: am/pm					
Snacks:					
Coffees/teas:	Fluid intake:	Totals:			

WEDNESDAY		kJ/Cal	Fat	Protein	Carbs
Breakfast Time: am/pm					
Lunch Time: am/pm					
Dinner Time: am/pm					
Snacks:					
Coffees/teas:	Fluid intake:	Totals:			

THURSDAY		kJ/Cal	Fat	Protein	Carbs
Breakfast Time: am/pm					
Lunch Time: am/pm					
Dinner Time: am/pm					
Snacks:					
Coffees/teas:	Fluid intake:	Totals:			

FRIDAY		kJ/Cal	Fat	Protein	Carbs
Breakfast Time: am/pm					
Lunch Time: am/pm					
Dinner Time: am/pm					
Snacks:					
Coffees/teas:	Fluid intake:	Totals:			

SATURDAY		kJ/Cal	Fat	Protein	Carbs
Breakfast Time: am/pm					
Lunch Time: am/pm					
Dinner Time: am/pm					
Snacks:					
Coffees/teas:	Fluid intake:	Totals:			

SUNDAY		kJ/Cal	Fat	Protein	Carbs
Breakfast Time: am/pm					
Lunch Time: am/pm					
Dinner Time: am/pm					
Snacks:					
Coffees/teas:	Fluid intake:	Totals:			

Units of alcohol this week: _____   Total alcohol kJ/Cal: _____

Vitamins and supplements

Weekly Totals	kJ/Cal	Fat	Protein	Carbs

Weekly Personal Summary

Energy level [1–5]   Stress level [1–5]

Hours of sleep   Sleep quality [1–5]

Mood [1–5]   Appetite [1–5]

kJ/Cal intake

Planned kJ/Cal	
Actual kJ/Cal	
Difference [+/-]	

Weight at start of week

Weight at end of week

BMI at start of week

BMI at end of week

Injuries or illnesses _____

Week Beginning

[ ] / [ ] / [ ]

Planned exercise sessions this week

	Exercise	Completed [Y/N]
Monday		
Tuesday		
Wednesday		
Thursday		
Friday		
Saturday		
Sunday		

Strength Training

MONDAY

Focus area	Equipment	SET 1		SET 2		SET 3		SET 4	
		Weight	Reps	Weight	Reps	Weight	Reps	Weight	Reps

TUESDAY

Focus area	Equipment	SET 1		SET 2		SET 3		SET 4	
		Weight	Reps	Weight	Reps	Weight	Reps	Weight	Reps

WEDNESDAY

Focus area	Equipment	SET 1		SET 2		SET 3		SET 4	
		Weight	Reps	Weight	Reps	Weight	Reps	Weight	Reps

THURSDAY

Focus area	Equipment	SET 1		SET 2		SET 3		SET 4	
		Weight	Reps	Weight	Reps	Weight	Reps	Weight	Reps

FRIDAY

Focus area	Equipment	SET 1		SET 2		SET 3		SET 4	
		Weight	Reps	Weight	Reps	Weight	Reps	Weight	Reps

SATURDAY

Focus area	Equipment	SET 1		SET 2		SET 3		SET 4	
		Weight	Reps	Weight	Reps	Weight	Reps	Weight	Reps

SUNDAY

Focus area	Equipment	SET 1		SET 2		SET 3		SET 4	
		Weight	Reps	Weight	Reps	Weight	Reps	Weight	Reps

Cardio Training

MONDAY	Exercise	Time	Distance/resistance	Intensity	Heart rate	Ease	kJ/Cal expended
							Total:

TUESDAY	Exercise	Time	Distance/resistance	Intensity	Heart rate	Ease	kJ/Cal expended
							Total:

WEDNESDAY	Exercise	Time	Distance/resistance	Intensity	Heart rate	Ease	kJ/Cal expended
							Total:

THURSDAY	Exercise	Time	Distance/resistance	Intensity	Heart rate	Ease	kJ/Cal expended
							Total:

FRIDAY	Exercise	Time	Distance/resistance	Intensity	Heart rate	Ease	kJ/Cal expended
							Total:

SATURDAY	Exercise	Time	Distance/resistance	Intensity	Heart rate	Ease	kJ/Cal expended
							Total:

SUNDAY	Exercise	Time	Distance/resistance	Intensity	Heart rate	Ease	kJ/Cal expended
							Total:

Weekly Total:

Food Diary

MONDAY		kJ/Cal	Fat	Protein	Carbs
Breakfast Time: am/pm					
Lunch Time: am/pm					
Dinner Time: am/pm					
Snacks:					
Coffees/teas:	**Fluid intake:**	**Totals:**			

TUESDAY		kJ/Cal	Fat	Protein	Carbs
Breakfast Time: am/pm					
Lunch Time: am/pm					
Dinner Time: am/pm					
Snacks:					
Coffees/teas:	**Fluid intake:**	**Totals:**			

WEDNESDAY		kJ/Cal	Fat	Protein	Carbs
Breakfast Time: am/pm					
Lunch Time: am/pm					
Dinner Time: am/pm					
Snacks:					
Coffees/teas:	**Fluid intake:**	**Totals:**			

THURSDAY		kJ/Cal	Fat	Protein	Carbs
Breakfast Time: am/pm					
Lunch Time: am/pm					
Dinner Time: am/pm					
Snacks:					
Coffees/teas:	**Fluid intake:**	**Totals:**			

FRIDAY		kJ/Cal	Fat	Protein	Carbs
Breakfast Time: am/pm					
Lunch Time: am/pm					
Dinner Time: am/pm					
Snacks:					
Coffees/teas:	Fluid intake:	Totals:			

SATURDAY		kJ/Cal	Fat	Protein	Carbs
Breakfast Time: am/pm					
Lunch Time: am/pm					
Dinner Time: am/pm					
Snacks:					
Coffees/teas:	Fluid intake:	Totals:			

SUNDAY		kJ/Cal	Fat	Protein	Carbs
Breakfast Time: am/pm					
Lunch Time: am/pm					
Dinner Time: am/pm					
Snacks:					
Coffees/teas:	Fluid intake:	Totals:			

Units of alcohol this week: **Total alcohol kJ/Cal:**

Vitamins and supplements

Weekly Totals	kJ/Cal	Fat	Protein	Carbs

Weekly Personal Summary

Energy level [1–5]   Stress level [1–5]

Hours of sleep [ ]   Sleep quality [1–5]

Mood [1–5]   Appetite [1–5]

Injuries or illnesses [   ]

kJ/Cal intake

Planned kJ/Cal	
Actual kJ/Cal	
Difference [+/-]	

Weight at start of week [   ]

Weight at end of week [   ]

BMI at start of week [   ]

BMI at end of week [   ]

Week Beginning

[/   /   ]

Planned exercise sessions this week

	Exercise	Completed [Y/N]
Monday		
Tuesday		
Wednesday		
Thursday		
Friday		
Saturday		
Sunday		

Strength Training

MONDAY

Focus area	Equipment	SET 1		SET 2		SET 3		SET 4	
		Weight	Reps	Weight	Reps	Weight	Reps	Weight	Reps

TUESDAY

Focus area	Equipment	SET 1		SET 2		SET 3		SET 4	
		Weight	Reps	Weight	Reps	Weight	Reps	Weight	Reps

WEDNESDAY

Focus area	Equipment	SET 1		SET 2		SET 3		SET 4	
		Weight	Reps	Weight	Reps	Weight	Reps	Weight	Reps

THURSDAY

Focus area	Equipment	SET 1		SET 2		SET 3		SET 4	
		Weight	Reps	Weight	Reps	Weight	Reps	Weight	Reps

FRIDAY

Focus area	Equipment	SET 1		SET 2		SET 3		SET 4	
		Weight	Reps	Weight	Reps	Weight	Reps	Weight	Reps

SATURDAY

Focus area	Equipment	SET 1		SET 2		SET 3		SET 4	
		Weight	Reps	Weight	Reps	Weight	Reps	Weight	Reps

SUNDAY

Focus area	Equipment	SET 1		SET 2		SET 3		SET 4	
		Weight	Reps	Weight	Reps	Weight	Reps	Weight	Reps

Cardio Training

MONDAY

Exercise	Time	Distance/resistance	Intensity	Heart rate	Ease	kJ/Cal expended
						Total:

TUESDAY

Exercise	Time	Distance/resistance	Intensity	Heart rate	Ease	kJ/Cal expended
						Total:

WEDNESDAY

Exercise	Time	Distance/resistance	Intensity	Heart rate	Ease	kJ/Cal expended
						Total:

THURSDAY

Exercise	Time	Distance/resistance	Intensity	Heart rate	Ease	kJ/Cal expended
						Total:

FRIDAY

Exercise	Time	Distance/resistance	Intensity	Heart rate	Ease	kJ/Cal expended
						Total:

SATURDAY

Exercise	Time	Distance/resistance	Intensity	Heart rate	Ease	kJ/Cal expended
						Total:

SUNDAY

Exercise	Time	Distance/resistance	Intensity	Heart rate	Ease	kJ/Cal expended
						Total:

Weekly Total:

Food Diary

MONDAY		kJ/Cal	Fat	Protein	Carbs
Breakfast Time: am/pm					
Lunch Time: am/pm					
Dinner Time: am/pm					
Snacks:					
Coffees/teas:	Fluid intake:	Totals:			

TUESDAY		kJ/Cal	Fat	Protein	Carbs
Breakfast Time: am/pm					
Lunch Time: am/pm					
Dinner Time: am/pm					
Snacks:					
Coffees/teas:	Fluid intake:	Totals:			

WEDNESDAY		kJ/Cal	Fat	Protein	Carbs
Breakfast Time: am/pm					
Lunch Time: am/pm					
Dinner Time: am/pm					
Snacks:					
Coffees/teas:	Fluid intake:	Totals:			

THURSDAY		kJ/Cal	Fat	Protein	Carbs
Breakfast Time: am/pm					
Lunch Time: am/pm					
Dinner Time: am/pm					
Snacks:					
Coffees/teas:	Fluid intake:	Totals:			

FRIDAY		kJ/Cal	Fat	Protein	Carbs
Breakfast Time: am/pm					
Lunch Time: am/pm					
Dinner Time: am/pm					
Snacks:					
Coffees/teas:	Fluid intake:	Totals:			

SATURDAY		kJ/Cal	Fat	Protein	Carbs
Breakfast Time: am/pm					
Lunch Time: am/pm					
Dinner Time: am/pm					
Snacks:					
Coffees/teas:	Fluid intake:	Totals:			

SUNDAY		kJ/Cal	Fat	Protein	Carbs
Breakfast Time: am/pm					
Lunch Time: am/pm					
Dinner Time: am/pm					
Snacks:					
Coffees/teas:	Fluid intake:	Totals:			

Units of alcohol this week: [   ]   Total alcohol kJ/Cal: [   ]

Vitamins and supplements

Weekly Totals	kJ/Cal	Fat	Protein	Carbs

Weekly Personal Summary

Energy level [ ] 1–5   Stress level [ ] 1–5

Hours of sleep [ ]   Sleep quality [ ] 1–5

Mood [ ] 1–5   Appetite [ ] 1–5

kJ/Cal intake

Planned kJ/Cal	
Actual kJ/Cal	
Difference [+/-]	

Weight at start of week [   ]

Weight at end of week [   ]

BMI at start of week [   ]

BMI at end of week [   ]

Injuries or illnesses [   ]

33

Week Beginning

[ ] / [ ] / [ ]

	Exercise	Completed [Y/N]
Monday		
Tuesday		
Wednesday		
Thursday		
Friday		
Saturday		
Sunday		

Strength Training

MONDAY

Focus area	Equipment	SET 1		SET 2		SET 3		SET 4	
		Weight	Reps	Weight	Reps	Weight	Reps	Weight	Reps

TUESDAY

Focus area	Equipment	SET 1		SET 2		SET 3		SET 4	
		Weight	Reps	Weight	Reps	Weight	Reps	Weight	Reps

WEDNESDAY

Focus area	Equipment	SET 1		SET 2		SET 3		SET 4	
		Weight	Reps	Weight	Reps	Weight	Reps	Weight	Reps

THURSDAY

Focus area	Equipment	SET 1		SET 2		SET 3		SET 4	
		Weight	Reps	Weight	Reps	Weight	Reps	Weight	Reps

FRIDAY

Focus area	Equipment	SET 1		SET 2		SET 3		SET 4	
		Weight	Reps	Weight	Reps	Weight	Reps	Weight	Reps

SATURDAY

Focus area	Equipment	SET 1		SET 2		SET 3		SET 4	
		Weight	Reps	Weight	Reps	Weight	Reps	Weight	Reps

SUNDAY

Focus area	Equipment	SET 1		SET 2		SET 3		SET 4	
		Weight	Reps	Weight	Reps	Weight	Reps	Weight	Reps

Cardio Training

MONDAY

Exercise	Time	Distance/resistance	Intensity	Heart rate	Ease	kJ/Cal expended
						Total:

TUESDAY

Exercise	Time	Distance/resistance	Intensity	Heart rate	Ease	kJ/Cal expended
						Total:

WEDNESDAY

Exercise	Time	Distance/resistance	Intensity	Heart rate	Ease	kJ/Cal expended
						Total:

THURSDAY

Exercise	Time	Distance/resistance	Intensity	Heart rate	Ease	kJ/Cal expended
						Total:

FRIDAY

Exercise	Time	Distance/resistance	Intensity	Heart rate	Ease	kJ/Cal expended
						Total:

SATURDAY

Exercise	Time	Distance/resistance	Intensity	Heart rate	Ease	kJ/Cal expended
						Total:

SUNDAY

Exercise	Time	Distance/resistance	Intensity	Heart rate	Ease	kJ/Cal expended
						Total:

Weekly Total:

Food Diary

MONDAY		kJ/Cal	Fat	Protein	Carbs
Breakfast Time: am/pm					
Lunch Time: am/pm					
Dinner Time: am/pm					
Snacks:					
Coffees/teas:	Fluid intake:	Totals:			

TUESDAY		kJ/Cal	Fat	Protein	Carbs
Breakfast Time: am/pm					
Lunch Time: am/pm					
Dinner Time: am/pm					
Snacks:					
Coffees/teas:	Fluid intake:	Totals:			

WEDNESDAY		kJ/Cal	Fat	Protein	Carbs
Breakfast Time: am/pm					
Lunch Time: am/pm					
Dinner Time: am/pm					
Snacks:					
Coffees/teas:	Fluid intake:	Totals:			

THURSDAY		kJ/Cal	Fat	Protein	Carbs
Breakfast Time: am/pm					
Lunch Time: am/pm					
Dinner Time: am/pm					
Snacks:					
Coffees/teas:	Fluid intake:	Totals:			

FRIDAY		kJ/Cal	Fat	Protein	Carbs
Breakfast Time: am/pm					
Lunch Time: am/pm					
Dinner Time: am/pm					
Snacks:					
Coffees/teas:	Fluid intake:	Totals:			

SATURDAY		kJ/Cal	Fat	Protein	Carbs
Breakfast Time: am/pm					
Lunch Time: am/pm					
Dinner Time: am/pm					
Snacks:					
Coffees/teas:	Fluid intake:	Totals:			

SUNDAY		kJ/Cal	Fat	Protein	Carbs
Breakfast Time: am/pm					
Lunch Time: am/pm					
Dinner Time: am/pm					
Snacks:					
Coffees/teas:	Fluid intake:	Totals:			

Units of alcohol this week: ☐   Total alcohol kJ/Cal: ☐

Vitamins and supplements

Weekly Totals	kJ/Cal	Fat	Protein	Carbs

Weekly Personal Summary

Energy level [1–5] ☐   Stress level [1–5] ☐

Hours of sleep ☐   Sleep quality [1–5] ☐

Mood [1–5] ☐   Appetite [1–5] ☐

kJ/Cal intake

Planned kJ/Cal	
Actual kJ/Cal	

Difference [+/-] ☐

Weight at start of week ☐
Weight at end of week ☐
BMI at start of week ☐
BMI at end of week ☐

Injuries or illnesses ☐

Week Beginning

[ ] / [ ] / [ ]

Planned exercise sessions this week

	Exercise	Completed [Y/N]
Monday		
Tuesday		
Wednesday		
Thursday		
Friday		
Saturday		
Sunday		

Strength Training

MONDAY

Focus area	Equipment	SET 1		SET 2		SET 3		SET 4	
		Weight	Reps	Weight	Reps	Weight	Reps	Weight	Reps

TUESDAY

Focus area	Equipment	SET 1		SET 2		SET 3		SET 4	
		Weight	Reps	Weight	Reps	Weight	Reps	Weight	Reps

WEDNESDAY

Focus area	Equipment	SET 1		SET 2		SET 3		SET 4	
		Weight	Reps	Weight	Reps	Weight	Reps	Weight	Reps

THURSDAY

Focus area	Equipment	SET 1		SET 2		SET 3		SET 4	
		Weight	Reps	Weight	Reps	Weight	Reps	Weight	Reps

FRIDAY

Focus area	Equipment	SET 1		SET 2		SET 3		SET 4	
		Weight	Reps	Weight	Reps	Weight	Reps	Weight	Reps

SATURDAY

Focus area	Equipment	SET 1		SET 2		SET 3		SET 4	
		Weight	Reps	Weight	Reps	Weight	Reps	Weight	Reps

SUNDAY

Focus area	Equipment	SET 1		SET 2		SET 3		SET 4	
		Weight	Reps	Weight	Reps	Weight	Reps	Weight	Reps

Cardio Training

	Exercise	Time	Distance/resistance	Intensity	Heart rate	Ease	kJ/Cal expended
MONDAY							
							Total:

	Exercise	Time	Distance/resistance	Intensity	Heart rate	Ease	kJ/Cal expended
TUESDAY							
							Total:

	Exercise	Time	Distance/resistance	Intensity	Heart rate	Ease	kJ/Cal expended
WEDNESDAY							
							Total:

	Exercise	Time	Distance/resistance	Intensity	Heart rate	Ease	kJ/Cal expended
THURSDAY							
							Total:

	Exercise	Time	Distance/resistance	Intensity	Heart rate	Ease	kJ/Cal expended
FRIDAY							
							Total:

	Exercise	Time	Distance/resistance	Intensity	Heart rate	Ease	kJ/Cal expended
SATURDAY							
							Total:

	Exercise	Time	Distance/resistance	Intensity	Heart rate	Ease	kJ/Cal expended
SUNDAY							
							Total:
							Weekly Total:

Food Diary

MONDAY		kJ/Cal	Fat	Protein	Carbs
Breakfast **Time:** am/pm					
Lunch **Time:** am/pm					
Dinner **Time:** am/pm					
Snacks:					
Coffees/teas:	**Fluid intake:**	**Totals:**			

TUESDAY		kJ/Cal	Fat	Protein	Carbs
Breakfast **Time:** am/pm					
Lunch **Time:** am/pm					
Dinner **Time:** am/pm					
Snacks:					
Coffees/teas:	**Fluid intake:**	**Totals:**			

WEDNESDAY		kJ/Cal	Fat	Protein	Carbs
Breakfast **Time:** am/pm					
Lunch **Time:** am/pm					
Dinner **Time:** am/pm					
Snacks:					
Coffees/teas:	**Fluid intake:**	**Totals:**			

THURSDAY		kJ/Cal	Fat	Protein	Carbs
Breakfast **Time:** am/pm					
Lunch **Time:** am/pm					
Dinner **Time:** am/pm					
Snacks:					
Coffees/teas:	**Fluid intake:**	**Totals:**			

FRIDAY		kJ/Cal	Fat	Protein	Carbs
Breakfast Time: am/pm					
Lunch Time: am/pm					
Dinner Time: am/pm					
Snacks:					
Coffees/teas:	Fluid intake:	**Totals:**			

SATURDAY		kJ/Cal	Fat	Protein	Carbs
Breakfast Time: am/pm					
Lunch Time: am/pm					
Dinner Time: am/pm					
Snacks:					
Coffees/teas:	Fluid intake:	**Totals:**			

SUNDAY		kJ/Cal	Fat	Protein	Carbs
Breakfast Time: am/pm					
Lunch Time: am/pm					
Dinner Time: am/pm					
Snacks:					
Coffees/teas:	Fluid intake:	**Totals:**			

Units of alcohol this week: **Total alcohol kJ/Cal:**

Vitamins and supplements

	kJ/Cal	Fat	Protein	Carbs
Weekly Totals				

Weekly Personal Summary

Energy level [1–5]   Stress level [1–5]

Hours of sleep   Sleep quality [1–5]

Mood [1–5]   Appetite [1–5]

kJ/Cal intake

Planned kJ/Cal	
Actual kJ/Cal	
Difference [+/-]	

Weight at start of week

Weight at end of week

BMI at start of week

BMI at end of week

Injuries or illnesses

Week Beginning

[/ /]

Planned exercise sessions this week

	Exercise	Completed [Y/N]
Monday		
Tuesday		
Wednesday		
Thursday		
Friday		
Saturday		
Sunday		

Strength Training

MONDAY

Focus area	Equipment	SET 1 Weight	SET 1 Reps	SET 2 Weight	SET 2 Reps	SET 3 Weight	SET 3 Reps	SET 4 Weight	SET 4 Reps

TUESDAY

Focus area	Equipment	SET 1 Weight	SET 1 Reps	SET 2 Weight	SET 2 Reps	SET 3 Weight	SET 3 Reps	SET 4 Weight	SET 4 Reps

WEDNESDAY

Focus area	Equipment	SET 1 Weight	SET 1 Reps	SET 2 Weight	SET 2 Reps	SET 3 Weight	SET 3 Reps	SET 4 Weight	SET 4 Reps

THURSDAY

Focus area	Equipment	SET 1 Weight	SET 1 Reps	SET 2 Weight	SET 2 Reps	SET 3 Weight	SET 3 Reps	SET 4 Weight	SET 4 Reps

FRIDAY

Focus area	Equipment	SET 1 Weight	SET 1 Reps	SET 2 Weight	SET 2 Reps	SET 3 Weight	SET 3 Reps	SET 4 Weight	SET 4 Reps

SATURDAY

Focus area	Equipment	SET 1 Weight	SET 1 Reps	SET 2 Weight	SET 2 Reps	SET 3 Weight	SET 3 Reps	SET 4 Weight	SET 4 Reps

SUNDAY

Focus area	Equipment	SET 1 Weight	SET 1 Reps	SET 2 Weight	SET 2 Reps	SET 3 Weight	SET 3 Reps	SET 4 Weight	SET 4 Reps

Cardio Training

MONDAY	Exercise	Time	Distance/resistance	Intensity	Heart rate	Ease	kJ/Cal expended
							Total:

TUESDAY	Exercise	Time	Distance/resistance	Intensity	Heart rate	Ease	kJ/Cal expended
							Total:

WEDNESDAY	Exercise	Time	Distance/resistance	Intensity	Heart rate	Ease	kJ/Cal expended
							Total:

THURSDAY	Exercise	Time	Distance/resistance	Intensity	Heart rate	Ease	kJ/Cal expended
							Total:

FRIDAY	Exercise	Time	Distance/resistance	Intensity	Heart rate	Ease	kJ/Cal expended
							Total:

SATURDAY	Exercise	Time	Distance/resistance	Intensity	Heart rate	Ease	kJ/Cal expended
							Total:

SUNDAY	Exercise	Time	Distance/resistance	Intensity	Heart rate	Ease	kJ/Cal expended
							Total:

Weekly Total:

Food Diary

MONDAY		kJ/Cal	Fat	Protein	Carbs
Breakfast Time: am/pm					
Lunch Time: am/pm					
Dinner Time: am/pm					
Snacks:					
Coffees/teas:	Fluid intake:	Totals:			

TUESDAY		kJ/Cal	Fat	Protein	Carbs
Breakfast Time: am/pm					
Lunch Time: am/pm					
Dinner Time: am/pm					
Snacks:					
Coffees/teas:	Fluid intake:	Totals:			

WEDNESDAY		kJ/Cal	Fat	Protein	Carbs
Breakfast Time: am/pm					
Lunch Time: am/pm					
Dinner TIme: am/pm					
Snacks:					
Coffees/teas:	Fluid intake:	Totals:			

THURSDAY		kJ/Cal	Fat	Protein	Carbs
Breakfast Time: am/pm					
Lunch Time: am/pm					
Dinner Time: am/pm					
Snacks:					
Coffees/teas:	Fluid intake:	Totals:			

FRIDAY			kJ/Cal	Fat	Protein	Carbs
Breakfast Time: am/pm						
Lunch Time: am/pm						
Dinner Time: am/pm						
Snacks:						
Coffees/teas:	Fluid intake:	Totals:				

SATURDAY			kJ/Cal	Fat	Protein	Carbs
Breakfast Time: am/pm						
Lunch Time: am/pm						
Dinner Time: am/pm						
Snacks:						
Coffees/teas:	Fluid intake:	Totals:				

SUNDAY			kJ/Cal	Fat	Protein	Carbs
Breakfast Time: am/pm						
Lunch Time: am/pm						
Dinner Time: am/pm						
Snacks:						
Coffees/teas:	Fluid intake:	Totals:				

Units of alcohol this week: _____ Total alcohol kJ/Cal: _____

Vitamins and supplements

Weekly Totals	kJ/Cal	Fat	Protein	Carbs

Weekly Personal Summary

Energy level 1–5 [ ]   Stress level 1–5 [ ]

kJ/Cal intake

Planned kJ/Cal	
Actual kJ/Cal	

Difference [+/-] [ ]

Hours of sleep [ ]   Sleep quality 1–5 [ ]

Mood 1–5 [ ]   Appetite 1–5 [ ]

Injuries or illnesses _____

Weight at start of week [ ]
Weight at end of week [ ]
BMI at start of week [ ]
BMI at end of week [ ]

Week Beginning

/ /

	Exercise	Completed [Y/N]
Monday		
Tuesday		
Wednesday		
Thursday		
Friday		
Saturday		
Sunday		

Strength Training

	Focus area	Equipment	SET 1 Weight	SET 1 Reps	SET 2 Weight	SET 2 Reps	SET 3 Weight	SET 3 Reps	SET 4 Weight	SET 4 Reps
MONDAY										
TUESDAY										
WEDNESDAY										
THURSDAY										
FRIDAY										
SATURDAY										
SUNDAY										

Cardio Training

MONDAY	Exercise	Time	Distance/resistance	Intensity	Heart rate	Ease	kJ/Cal expended
							Total:

TUESDAY	Exercise	Time	Distance/resistance	Intensity	Heart rate	Ease	kJ/Cal expended
							Total:

WEDNESDAY	Exercise	Time	Distance/resistance	Intensity	Heart rate	Ease	kJ/Cal expended
							Total:

THURSDAY	Exercise	Time	Distance/resistance	Intensity	Heart rate	Ease	kJ/Cal expended
							Total:

FRIDAY	Exercise	Time	Distance/resistance	Intensity	Heart rate	Ease	kJ/Cal expended
							Total:

SATURDAY	Exercise	Time	Distance/resistance	Intensity	Heart rate	Ease	kJ/Cal expended
							Total:

SUNDAY	Exercise	Time	Distance/resistance	Intensity	Heart rate	Ease	kJ/Cal expended
							Total:

Weekly Total:

Food Diary

MONDAY		kJ/Cal	Fat	Protein	Carbs
Breakfast Time: am/pm					
Lunch Time: am/pm					
Dinner Time: am/pm					
Snacks:					
Coffees/teas:	Fluid intake:	**Totals:**			

TUESDAY		kJ/Cal	Fat	Protein	Carbs
Breakfast Time: am/pm					
Lunch Time: am/pm					
Dinner Time: am/pm					
Snacks:					
Coffees/teas:	Fluid intake:	**Totals:**			

WEDNESDAY		kJ/Cal	Fat	Protein	Carbs
Breakfast Time: am/pm					
Lunch Time: am/pm					
Dinner Time: am/pm					
Snacks:					
Coffees/teas:	Fluid intake:	**Totals:**			

THURSDAY		kJ/Cal	Fat	Protein	Carbs
Breakfast Time: am/pm					
Lunch Time: am/pm					
Dinner Time: am/pm					
Snacks:					
Coffees/teas:	Fluid intake:	**Totals:**			

FRIDAY		kJ/Cal	Fat	Protein	Carbs
Breakfast Time: am/pm					
Lunch Time: am/pm					
Dinner Time: am/pm					
Snacks:					
Coffees/teas:	Fluid intake:	Totals:			

SATURDAY		kJ/Cal	Fat	Protein	Carbs
Breakfast Time: am/pm					
Lunch Time: am/pm					
Dinner Time: am/pm					
Snacks:					
Coffees/teas:	Fluid intake:	Totals:			

SUNDAY		kJ/Cal	Fat	Protein	Carbs
Breakfast Time: am/pm					
Lunch Time: am/pm					
Dinner Time: am/pm					
Snacks:					
Coffees/teas:	Fluid intake:	Totals:			

Units of alcohol this week: [ ]   Total alcohol kJ/Cal: [ ]

Vitamins and supplements

Weekly Totals	kJ/Cal	Fat	Protein	Carbs

Weekly Personal Summary

Energy level 1–5 [ ]   Stress level 1–5 [ ]

Hours of sleep [ ]   Sleep quality 1–5 [ ]

Mood 1–5 [ ]   Appetite 1–5 [ ]

kJ/Cal intake

Planned kJ/Cal	
Actual kJ/Cal	

Difference [+/-] [ ]

Weight at start of week [ ]

Weight at end of week [ ]

BMI at start of week [ ]

BMI at end of week [ ]

Injuries or illnesses [ ]

Week Beginning

/ /

	Exercise	Completed [Y/N]
Monday		
Tuesday		
Wednesday		
Thursday		
Friday		
Saturday		
Sunday		

Strength Training

MONDAY

Focus area	Equipment	SET 1		SET 2		SET 3		SET 4	
		Weight	Reps	Weight	Reps	Weight	Reps	Weight	Reps

TUESDAY

Focus area	Equipment	SET 1		SET 2		SET 3		SET 4	
		Weight	Reps	Weight	Reps	Weight	Reps	Weight	Reps

WEDNESDAY

Focus area	Equipment	SET 1		SET 2		SET 3		SET 4	
		Weight	Reps	Weight	Reps	Weight	Reps	Weight	Reps

THURSDAY

Focus area	Equipment	SET 1		SET 2		SET 3		SET 4	
		Weight	Reps	Weight	Reps	Weight	Reps	Weight	Reps

FRIDAY

Focus area	Equipment	SET 1		SET 2		SET 3		SET 4	
		Weight	Reps	Weight	Reps	Weight	Reps	Weight	Reps

SATURDAY

Focus area	Equipment	SET 1		SET 2		SET 3		SET 4	
		Weight	Reps	Weight	Reps	Weight	Reps	Weight	Reps

SUNDAY

Focus area	Equipment	SET 1		SET 2		SET 3		SET 4	
		Weight	Reps	Weight	Reps	Weight	Reps	Weight	Reps

Cardio Training

MONDAY

Exercise	Time	Distance/resistance	Intensity	Heart rate	Ease	kJ/Cal expended
						Total:

TUESDAY

Exercise	Time	Distance/resistance	Intensity	Heart rate	Ease	kJ/Cal expended
						Total:

WEDNESDAY

Exercise	Time	Distance/resistance	Intensity	Heart rate	Ease	kJ/Cal expended
						Total:

THURSDAY

Exercise	Time	Distance/resistance	Intensity	Heart rate	Ease	kJ/Cal expended
						Total:

FRIDAY

Exercise	Time	Distance/resistance	Intensity	Heart rate	Ease	kJ/Cal expended
						Total:

SATURDAY

Exercise	Time	Distance/resistance	Intensity	Heart rate	Ease	kJ/Cal expended
						Total:

SUNDAY

Exercise	Time	Distance/resistance	Intensity	Heart rate	Ease	kJ/Cal expended
						Total:

Weekly Total:

Food Diary

MONDAY		kJ/Cal	Fat	Protein	Carbs
Breakfast Time: am/pm					
Lunch Time: am/pm					
Dinner Time: am/pm					
Snacks:					
Coffees/teas:	Fluid intake: Totals:				

TUESDAY		kJ/Cal	Fat	Protein	Carbs
Breakfast Time: am/pm					
Lunch Time: am/pm					
Dinner Time: am/pm					
Snacks:					
Coffees/teas:	Fluid intake: Totals:				

WEDNESDAY		kJ/Cal	Fat	Protein	Carbs
Breakfast Time: am/pm					
Lunch Time: am/pm					
Dinner Time: am/pm					
Snacks:					
Coffees/teas:	Fluid intake: Totals:				

THURSDAY		kJ/Cal	Fat	Protein	Carbs
Breakfast Time: am/pm					
Lunch Time: am/pm					
Dinner Time: am/pm					
Snacks:					
Coffees/teas:	Fluid intake: Totals:				

FRIDAY			kJ/Cal	Fat	Protein	Carbs
Breakfast Time: am/pm						
Lunch Time: am/pm						
Dinner Time: am/pm						
Snacks:						
Coffees/teas:	Fluid intake:	Totals:				

SATURDAY			kJ/Cal	Fat	Protein	Carbs
Breakfast Time: am/pm						
Lunch Time: am/pm						
Dinner Time: am/pm						
Snacks:						
Coffees/teas:	Fluid intake:	Totals:				

SUNDAY			kJ/Cal	Fat	Protein	Carbs
Breakfast Time: am/pm						
Lunch Time: am/pm						
Dinner Time: am/pm						
Snacks:						
Coffees/teas:	Fluid intake:	Totals:				

Units of alcohol this week: [ ]   Total alcohol kJ/Cal: [ ]

Vitamins and supplements

Weekly Totals	kJ/Cal	Fat	Protein	Carbs

Weekly Personal Summary

Energy level [1–5] [ ]   Stress level [1–5] [ ]

Hours of sleep [ ]   Sleep quality [1–5] [ ]

Mood [1–5] [ ]   Appetite [1–5] [ ]

kJ/Cal intake

| Planned kJ/Cal | |
| Actual kJ/Cal | |

Difference [+/-] [ ]

Weight at start of week [ ]

Weight at end of week [ ]

BMI at start of week [ ]

BMI at end of week [ ]

Injuries or illnesses [ ]

Week Beginning

| / / |

Planned exercise sessions this week

	Exercise	Completed [Y/N]
Monday		
Tuesday		
Wednesday		
Thursday		
Friday		
Saturday		
Sunday		

Strength Training

MONDAY

Focus area	Equipment	SET 1		SET 2		SET 3		SET 4	
		Weight	Reps	Weight	Reps	Weight	Reps	Weight	Reps

TUESDAY

Focus area	Equipment	SET 1		SET 2		SET 3		SET 4	
		Weight	Reps	Weight	Reps	Weight	Reps	Weight	Reps

WEDNESDAY

Focus area	Equipment	SET 1		SET 2		SET 3		SET 4	
		Weight	Reps	Weight	Reps	Weight	Reps	Weight	Reps

THURSDAY

Focus area	Equipment	SET 1		SET 2		SET 3		SET 4	
		Weight	Reps	Weight	Reps	Weight	Reps	Weight	Reps

FRIDAY

Focus area	Equipment	SET 1		SET 2		SET 3		SET 4	
		Weight	Reps	Weight	Reps	Weight	Reps	Weight	Reps

SATURDAY

Focus area	Equipment	SET 1		SET 2		SET 3		SET 4	
		Weight	Reps	Weight	Reps	Weight	Reps	Weight	Reps

SUNDAY

Focus area	Equipment	SET 1		SET 2		SET 3		SET 4	
		Weight	Reps	Weight	Reps	Weight	Reps	Weight	Reps

Cardio Training

MONDAY

Exercise	Time	Distance/resistance	Intensity	Heart rate	Ease	kJ/Cal expended
						Total:

TUESDAY

Exercise	Time	Distance/resistance	Intensity	Heart rate	Ease	kJ/Cal expended
						Total:

WEDNESDAY

Exercise	Time	Distance/resistance	Intensity	Heart rate	Ease	kJ/Cal expended
						Total:

THURSDAY

Exercise	Time	Distance/resistance	Intensity	Heart rate	Ease	kJ/Cal expended
						Total:

FRIDAY

Exercise	Time	Distance/resistance	Intensity	Heart rate	Ease	kJ/Cal expended
						Total:

SATURDAY

Exercise	Time	Distance/resistance	Intensity	Heart rate	Ease	kJ/Cal expended
						Total:

SUNDAY

Exercise	Time	Distance/resistance	Intensity	Heart rate	Ease	kJ/Cal expended
						Total:

Weekly Total:

Food Diary

MONDAY		kJ/Cal	Fat	Protein	Carbs
Breakfast Time: am/pm					
Lunch Time: am/pm					
Dinner Time: am/pm					
Snacks:					
Coffees/teas:	Fluid intake: Totals:				

TUESDAY		kJ/Cal	Fat	Protein	Carbs
Breakfast Time: am/pm					
Lunch Time: am/pm					
Dinner Time: am/pm					
Snacks:					
Coffees/teas:	Fluid intake: Totals:				

WEDNESDAY		kJ/Cal	Fat	Protein	Carbs
Breakfast Time: am/pm					
Lunch Time: am/pm					
Dinner Time: am/pm					
Snacks:					
Coffees/teas:	Fluid intake: Totals:				

THURSDAY		kJ/Cal	Fat	Protein	Carbs
Breakfast Time: am/pm					
Lunch Time: am/pm					
Dinner Time: am/pm					
Snacks:					
Coffees/teas:	Fluid intake: Totals:				

FRIDAY			kJ/Cal	Fat	Protein	Carbs
Breakfast Time: am/pm						
Lunch Time: am/pm						
Dinner Time: am/pm						
Snacks:						
Coffees/teas:	Fluid intake:	Totals:				

SATURDAY			kJ/Cal	Fat	Protein	Carbs
Breakfast Time: am/pm						
Lunch Time: am/pm						
Dinner Time: am/pm						
Snacks:						
Coffees/teas:	Fluid intake:	Totals:				

SUNDAY			kJ/Cal	Fat	Protein	Carbs
Breakfast Time: am/pm						
Lunch Time: am/pm						
Dinner Time: am/pm						
Snacks:						
Coffees/teas:	Fluid intake:	Totals:				

Units of alcohol this week: Total alcohol kJ/Cal:

Vitamins and supplements

Weekly Totals	kJ/Cal	Fat	Protein	Carbs

Weekly Personal Summary

Energy level 1–5   Stress level 1–5

Hours of sleep   Sleep quality 1–5

Mood 1–5   Appetite 1–5

kJ/Cal intake

Planned kJ/Cal	
Actual kJ/Cal	

Difference [+/-]

Weight at start of week

Weight at end of week

BMI at start of week

BMI at end of week

Injuries or illnesses

Week Beginning

[ ] / [ ] / [ ]

Planned exercise sessions this week

	Exercise	Completed [Y/N]
Monday		
Tuesday		
Wednesday		
Thursday		
Friday		
Saturday		
Sunday		

Strength Training

MONDAY

Focus area	Equipment	SET 1 Weight	SET 1 Reps	SET 2 Weight	SET 2 Reps	SET 3 Weight	SET 3 Reps	SET 4 Weight	SET 4 Reps

TUESDAY

Focus area	Equipment	SET 1 Weight	SET 1 Reps	SET 2 Weight	SET 2 Reps	SET 3 Weight	SET 3 Reps	SET 4 Weight	SET 4 Reps

WEDNESDAY

Focus area	Equipment	SET 1 Weight	SET 1 Reps	SET 2 Weight	SET 2 Reps	SET 3 Weight	SET 3 Reps	SET 4 Weight	SET 4 Reps

THURSDAY

Focus area	Equipment	SET 1 Weight	SET 1 Reps	SET 2 Weight	SET 2 Reps	SET 3 Weight	SET 3 Reps	SET 4 Weight	SET 4 Reps

FRIDAY

Focus area	Equipment	SET 1 Weight	SET 1 Reps	SET 2 Weight	SET 2 Reps	SET 3 Weight	SET 3 Reps	SET 4 Weight	SET 4 Reps

SATURDAY

Focus area	Equipment	SET 1 Weight	SET 1 Reps	SET 2 Weight	SET 2 Reps	SET 3 Weight	SET 3 Reps	SET 4 Weight	SET 4 Reps

SUNDAY

Focus area	Equipment	SET 1 Weight	SET 1 Reps	SET 2 Weight	SET 2 Reps	SET 3 Weight	SET 3 Reps	SET 4 Weight	SET 4 Reps

Cardio Training

MONDAY

Exercise	Time	Distance/resistance	Intensity	Heart rate	Ease	kJ/Cal expended
						Total:

TUESDAY

Exercise	Time	Distance/resistance	Intensity	Heart rate	Ease	kJ/Cal expended
						Total:

WEDNESDAY

Exercise	Time	Distance/resistance	Intensity	Heart rate	Ease	kJ/Cal expended
						Total:

THURSDAY

Exercise	Time	Distance/resistance	Intensity	Heart rate	Ease	kJ/Cal expended
						Total:

FRIDAY

Exercise	Time	Distance/resistance	Intensity	Heart rate	Ease	kJ/Cal expended
						Total:

SATURDAY

Exercise	Time	Distance/resistance	Intensity	Heart rate	Ease	kJ/Cal expended
						Total:

SUNDAY

Exercise	Time	Distance/resistance	Intensity	Heart rate	Ease	kJ/Cal expended
						Total:

Weekly Total:

Food Diary

MONDAY		kJ/Cal	Fat	Protein	Carbs
Breakfast Time: am/pm					
Lunch Time: am/pm					
Dinner Time: am/pm					
Snacks:					
Coffees/teas:	Fluid intake: Totals:				

TUESDAY		kJ/Cal	Fat	Protein	Carbs
Breakfast Time: am/pm					
Lunch Time: am/pm					
Dinner Time: am/pm					
Snacks:					
Coffees/teas:	Fluid intake: Totals:				

WEDNESDAY		kJ/Cal	Fat	Protein	Carbs
Breakfast Time: am/pm					
Lunch Time: am/pm					
Dinner Time: am/pm					
Snacks:					
Coffees/teas:	Fluid intake: Totals:				

THURSDAY		kJ/Cal	Fat	Protein	Carbs
Breakfast Time: am/pm					
Lunch Time: am/pm					
Dinner Time: am/pm					
Snacks:					
Coffees/teas:	Fluid intake: Totals:				

FRIDAY			kJ/Cal	Fat	Protein	Carbs
Breakfast Time: am/pm						
Lunch Time: am/pm						
Dinner Time: am/pm						
Snacks:						
Coffees/teas:	Fluid intake:	Totals:				

SATURDAY			kJ/Cal	Fat	Protein	Carbs
Breakfast Time: am/pm						
Lunch Time: am/pm						
Dinner Time: am/pm						
Snacks:						
Coffees/teas:	Fluid intake:	Totals:				

SUNDAY			kJ/Cal	Fat	Protein	Carbs
Breakfast Time: am/pm						
Lunch Time: am/pm						
Dinner Time: am/pm						
Snacks:						
Coffees/teas:	Fluid intake:	Totals:				

Units of alcohol this week: _____   Total alcohol kJ/Cal: _____

Vitamins and supplements

Weekly Totals	kJ/Cal	Fat	Protein	Carbs

Weekly Personal Summary

Energy level [1–5]   Stress level [1–5]   **kJ/Cal intake**

| Planned kJ/Cal | |
| Actual kJ/Cal | |

Difference [+/-] _____

Hours of sleep _____   Sleep quality [1–5]

Mood [1–5]   Appetite [1–5]

Weight at start of week _____

Weight at end of week _____

BMI at start of week _____

BMI at end of week _____

Injuries or illnesses _____

Week Beginning

Planned exercise sessions this week

	Exercise	Completed [Y/N]
Monday		
Tuesday		
Wednesday		
Thursday		
Friday		
Saturday		
Sunday		

Strength Training

MONDAY

Focus area	Equipment	SET 1		SET 2		SET 3		SET 4	
		Weight	Reps	Weight	Reps	Weight	Reps	Weight	Reps

TUESDAY

Focus area	Equipment	SET 1		SET 2		SET 3		SET 4	
		Weight	Reps	Weight	Reps	Weight	Reps	Weight	Reps

WEDNESDAY

Focus area	Equipment	SET 1		SET 2		SET 3		SET 4	
		Weight	Reps	Weight	Reps	Weight	Reps	Weight	Reps

THURSDAY

Focus area	Equipment	SET 1		SET 2		SET 3		SET 4	
		Weight	Reps	Weight	Reps	Weight	Reps	Weight	Reps

FRIDAY

Focus area	Equipment	SET 1		SET 2		SET 3		SET 4	
		Weight	Reps	Weight	Reps	Weight	Reps	Weight	Reps

SATURDAY

Focus area	Equipment	SET 1		SET 2		SET 3		SET 4	
		Weight	Reps	Weight	Reps	Weight	Reps	Weight	Reps

SUNDAY

Focus area	Equipment	SET 1		SET 2		SET 3		SET 4	
		Weight	Reps	Weight	Reps	Weight	Reps	Weight	Reps

Cardio Training

MONDAY

Exercise	Time	Distance/resistance	Intensity	Heart rate	Ease	kJ/Cal expended
						Total:

TUESDAY

Exercise	Time	Distance/resistance	Intensity	Heart rate	Ease	kJ/Cal expended
						Total:

WEDNESDAY

Exercise	Time	Distance/resistance	Intensity	Heart rate	Ease	kJ/Cal expended
						Total:

THURSDAY

Exercise	Time	Distance/resistance	Intensity	Heart rate	Ease	kJ/Cal expended
						Total:

FRIDAY

Exercise	Time	Distance/resistance	Intensity	Heart rate	Ease	kJ/Cal expended
						Total:

SATURDAY

Exercise	Time	Distance/resistance	Intensity	Heart rate	Ease	kJ/Cal expended
						Total:

SUNDAY

Exercise	Time	Distance/resistance	Intensity	Heart rate	Ease	kJ/Cal expended
						Total:

Weekly Total:

Food Diary

MONDAY		kJ/Cal	Fat	Protein	Carbs
Breakfast Time: am/pm					
Lunch Time: am/pm					
Dinner Time: am/pm					
Snacks:					
Coffees/teas:	Fluid intake: Totals:				

TUESDAY		kJ/Cal	Fat	Protein	Carbs
Breakfast Time: am/pm					
Lunch Time: am/pm					
Dinner Time: am/pm					
Snacks:					
Coffees/teas:	Fluid intake: Totals:				

WEDNESDAY		kJ/Cal	Fat	Protein	Carbs
Breakfast Time: am/pm					
Lunch Time: am/pm					
Dinner Time: am/pm					
Snacks:					
Coffees/teas:	Fluid intake: Totals:				

THURSDAY		kJ/Cal	Fat	Protein	Carbs
Breakfast Time: am/pm					
Lunch Time: am/pm					
Dinner Time: am/pm					
Snacks:					
Coffees/teas:	Fluid intake: Totals:				

FRIDAY		kJ/Cal	Fat	Protein	Carbs
Breakfast Time: am/pm					
Lunch Time: am/pm					
Dinner Time: am/pm					
Snacks:					
Coffees/teas:	Fluid intake: Totals:				

SATURDAY		kJ/Cal	Fat	Protein	Carbs
Breakfast Time: am/pm					
Lunch Time: am/pm					
Dinner Time: am/pm					
Snacks:					
Coffees/teas:	Fluid intake: Totals:				

SUNDAY		kJ/Cal	Fat	Protein	Carbs
Breakfast Time: am/pm					
Lunch Time: am/pm					
Dinner Time: am/pm					
Snacks:					
Coffees/teas:	Fluid intake: Totals:				

Units of alcohol this week: ▭   Total alcohol kJ/Cal: ▭

Vitamins and supplements

Weekly Totals	kJ/Cal	Fat	Protein	Carbs

Weekly Personal Summary

Energy level ▭ 1–5   Stress level ▭ 1–5

Hours of sleep ▭   Sleep quality ▭ 1–5

Mood ▭ 1–5   Appetite ▭ 1–5

kJ/Cal intake

Planned kJ/Cal	
Actual kJ/Cal	

Difference [+/-] ▭

Weight at start of week ▭

Weight at end of week ▭

BMI at start of week ▭

BMI at end of week ▭

Injuries or illnesses ▭

Week Beginning

[ ] / [ ] / [ ]

Planned exercise sessions this week

	Exercise	Completed [Y/N]
Monday		
Tuesday		
Wednesday		
Thursday		
Friday		
Saturday		
Sunday		

Strength Training

MONDAY

Focus area	Equipment	SET 1		SET 2		SET 3		SET 4	
		Weight	Reps	Weight	Reps	Weight	Reps	Weight	Reps

TUESDAY

Focus area	Equipment	SET 1		SET 2		SET 3		SET 4	
		Weight	Reps	Weight	Reps	Weight	Reps	Weight	Reps

WEDNESDAY

Focus area	Equipment	SET 1		SET 2		SET 3		SET 4	
		Weight	Reps	Weight	Reps	Weight	Reps	Weight	Reps

THURSDAY

Focus area	Equipment	SET 1		SET 2		SET 3		SET 4	
		Weight	Reps	Weight	Reps	Weight	Reps	Weight	Reps

FRIDAY

Focus area	Equipment	SET 1		SET 2		SET 3		SET 4	
		Weight	Reps	Weight	Reps	Weight	Reps	Weight	Reps

SATURDAY

Focus area	Equipment	SET 1		SET 2		SET 3		SET 4	
		Weight	Reps	Weight	Reps	Weight	Reps	Weight	Reps

SUNDAY

Focus area	Equipment	SET 1		SET 2		SET 3		SET 4	
		Weight	Reps	Weight	Reps	Weight	Reps	Weight	Reps

Cardio Training

	Exercise	Time	Distance/resistance	Intensity	Heart rate	Ease	kJ/Cal expended
MONDAY							
							Total:

	Exercise	Time	Distance/resistance	Intensity	Heart rate	Ease	kJ/Cal expended
TUESDAY							
							Total:

	Exercise	Time	Distance/resistance	Intensity	Heart rate	Ease	kJ/Cal expended
WEDNESDAY							
							Total:

	Exercise	Time	Distance/resistance	Intensity	Heart rate	Ease	kJ/Cal expended
THURSDAY							
							Total:

	Exercise	Time	Distance/resistance	Intensity	Heart rate	Ease	kJ/Cal expended
FRIDAY							
							Total:

	Exercise	Time	Distance/resistance	Intensity	Heart rate	Ease	kJ/Cal expended
SATURDAY							
							Total:

	Exercise	Time	Distance/resistance	Intensity	Heart rate	Ease	kJ/Cal expended
SUNDAY							
							Total:

Weekly Total:

Food Diary

MONDAY		kJ/Cal	Fat	Protein	Carbs
Breakfast Time: am/pm					
Lunch Time: am/pm					
Dinner Time: am/pm					
Snacks:					
Coffees/teas:	Fluid intake:	Totals:			

TUESDAY		kJ/Cal	Fat	Protein	Carbs
Breakfast Time: am/pm					
Lunch Time: am/pm					
Dinner Time: am/pm					
Snacks:					
Coffees/teas:	Fluid intake:	Totals:			

WEDNESDAY		kJ/Cal	Fat	Protein	Carbs
Breakfast Time: am/pm					
Lunch Time: am/pm					
Dinner Time: am/pm					
Snacks:					
Coffees/teas:	Fluid intake:	Totals:			

THURSDAY		kJ/Cal	Fat	Protein	Carbs
Breakfast Time: am/pm					
Lunch Time: am/pm					
Dinner Time: am/pm					
Snacks:					
Coffees/teas:	Fluid intake:	Totals:			

FRIDAY		kJ/Cal	Fat	Protein	Carbs
Breakfast Time: am/pm					
Lunch Time: am/pm					
Dinner Time: am/pm					
Snacks:					
Coffees/teas:	**Fluid intake:**	**Totals:**			

SATURDAY		kJ/Cal	Fat	Protein	Carbs
Breakfast Time: am/pm					
Lunch Time: am/pm					
Dinner Time: am/pm					
Snacks:					
Coffees/teas:	**Fluid intake:**	**Totals:**			

SUNDAY		kJ/Cal	Fat	Protein	Carbs
Breakfast Time: am/pm					
Lunch Time: am/pm					
Dinner Time: am/pm					
Snacks:					
Coffees/teas:	**Fluid intake:**	**Totals:**			

Units of alcohol this week: Total alcohol kJ/Cal:

Vitamins and supplements

Weekly Totals	kJ/Cal	Fat	Protein	Carbs

Weekly Personal Summary

Energy level [1–5]　　Stress level [1–5]

Hours of sleep　　Sleep quality [1–5]

Mood [1–5]　　Appetite [1–5]

Injuries or illnesses

kJ/Cal intake

Planned kJ/Cal	
Actual kJ/Cal	
Difference [+/-]	

Weight at start of week

Weight at end of week

BMI at start of week

BMI at end of week

Week Beginning

[ ] / [ ] / [ ]

Planned exercise sessions this week

	Exercise	Completed [Y/N]
Monday		
Tuesday		
Wednesday		
Thursday		
Friday		
Saturday		
Sunday		

Strength Training

MONDAY

Focus area	Equipment	SET 1		SET 2		SET 3		SET 4	
		Weight	Reps	Weight	Reps	Weight	Reps	Weight	Reps

TUESDAY

Focus area	Equipment	SET 1		SET 2		SET 3		SET 4	
		Weight	Reps	Weight	Reps	Weight	Reps	Weight	Reps

WEDNESDAY

Focus area	Equipment	SET 1		SET 2		SET 3		SET 4	
		Weight	Reps	Weight	Reps	Weight	Reps	Weight	Reps

THURSDAY

Focus area	Equipment	SET 1		SET 2		SET 3		SET 4	
		Weight	Reps	Weight	Reps	Weight	Reps	Weight	Reps

FRIDAY

Focus area	Equipment	SET 1		SET 2		SET 3		SET 4	
		Weight	Reps	Weight	Reps	Weight	Reps	Weight	Reps

SATURDAY

Focus area	Equipment	SET 1		SET 2		SET 3		SET 4	
		Weight	Reps	Weight	Reps	Weight	Reps	Weight	Reps

SUNDAY

Focus area	Equipment	SET 1		SET 2		SET 3		SET 4	
		Weight	Reps	Weight	Reps	Weight	Reps	Weight	Reps

Cardio Training

	Exercise	Time	Distance/resistance	Intensity	Heart rate	Ease	kJ/Cal expended
MONDAY							
							Total:

	Exercise	Time	Distance/resistance	Intensity	Heart rate	Ease	kJ/Cal expended
TUESDAY							
							Total:

	Exercise	Time	Distance/resistance	Intensity	Heart rate	Ease	kJ/Cal expended
WEDNESDAY							
							Total:

	Exercise	Time	Distance/resistance	Intensity	Heart rate	Ease	kJ/Cal expended
THURSDAY							
							Total:

	Exercise	Time	Distance/resistance	Intensity	Heart rate	Ease	kJ/Cal expended
FRIDAY							
							Total:

	Exercise	Time	Distance/resistance	Intensity	Heart rate	Ease	kJ/Cal expended
SATURDAY							
							Total:

	Exercise	Time	Distance/resistance	Intensity	Heart rate	Ease	kJ/Cal expended
SUNDAY							
							Total:

Weekly Total:

Food Diary

MONDAY		kJ/Cal	Fat	Protein	Carbs
Breakfast Time: am/pm					
Lunch Time: am/pm					
Dinner Time: am/pm					
Snacks:					
Coffees/teas:	Fluid intake: Totals:				

TUESDAY		kJ/Cal	Fat	Protein	Carbs
Breakfast Time: am/pm					
Lunch Time: am/pm					
Dinner Time: am/pm					
Snacks:					
Coffees/teas:	Fluid intake: Totals:				

WEDNESDAY		kJ/Cal	Fat	Protein	Carbs
Breakfast Time: am/pm					
Lunch Time: am/pm					
Dinner Time: am/pm					
Snacks:					
Coffees/teas:	Fluid intake: Totals:				

THURSDAY		kJ/Cal	Fat	Protein	Carbs
Breakfast Time: am/pm					
Lunch Time: am/pm					
Dinner Time: am/pm					
Snacks:					
Coffees/teas:	Fluid intake: Totals:				

FRIDAY			kJ/Cal	Fat	Protein	Carbs
Breakfast Time: am/pm						
Lunch Time: am/pm						
Dinner Time: am/pm						
Snacks:						
Coffees/teas:	Fluid intake:	Totals:				

SATURDAY			kJ/Cal	Fat	Protein	Carbs
Breakfast Time: am/pm						
Lunch Time: am/pm						
Dinner Time: am/pm						
Snacks:						
Coffees/teas:	Fluid intake:	Totals:				

SUNDAY			kJ/Cal	Fat	Protein	Carbs
Breakfast Time: am/pm						
Lunch Time: am/pm						
Dinner Time: am/pm						
Snacks:						
Coffees/teas:	Fluid intake:	Totals:				

Units of alcohol this week: Total alcohol kJ/Cal:

Vitamins and supplements

Weekly Totals	kJ/Cal	Fat	Protein	Carbs

Weekly Personal Summary

Energy level [ ] 1–5   Stress level [ ] 1–5

Hours of sleep [ ]   Sleep quality [ ] 1–5

Mood [ ] 1–5   Appetite [ ] 1–5

kJ/Cal intake

Planned kJ/Cal	
Actual kJ/Cal	
Difference [+/-]	

Weight at start of week [ ]

Weight at end of week [ ]

BMI at start of week [ ]

BMI at end of week [ ]

Injuries or illnesses [ ]

Week Beginning

[/   /   ]

Planned exercise sessions this week

	Exercise	Completed [Y/N]
Monday		
Tuesday		
Wednesday		
Thursday		
Friday		
Saturday		
Sunday		

Strength Training

MONDAY

Focus area	Equipment	SET 1 Weight	Reps	SET 2 Weight	Reps	SET 3 Weight	Reps	SET 4 Weight	Reps

TUESDAY

Focus area	Equipment	SET 1 Weight	Reps	SET 2 Weight	Reps	SET 3 Weight	Reps	SET 4 Weight	Reps

WEDNESDAY

Focus area	Equipment	SET 1 Weight	Reps	SET 2 Weight	Reps	SET 3 Weight	Reps	SET 4 Weight	Reps

THURSDAY

Focus area	Equipment	SET 1 Weight	Reps	SET 2 Weight	Reps	SET 3 Weight	Reps	SET 4 Weight	Reps

FRIDAY

Focus area	Equipment	SET 1 Weight	Reps	SET 2 Weight	Reps	SET 3 Weight	Reps	SET 4 Weight	Reps

SATURDAY

Focus area	Equipment	SET 1 Weight	Reps	SET 2 Weight	Reps	SET 3 Weight	Reps	SET 4 Weight	Reps

SUNDAY

Focus area	Equipment	SET 1 Weight	Reps	SET 2 Weight	Reps	SET 3 Weight	Reps	SET 4 Weight	Reps

Cardio Training

MONDAY

	Exercise	Time	Distance/resistance	Intensity	Heart rate	Ease	kJ/Cal expended
							Total:

TUESDAY

	Exercise	Time	Distance/resistance	Intensity	Heart rate	Ease	kJ/Cal expended
							Total:

WEDNESDAY

	Exercise	Time	Distance/resistance	Intensity	Heart rate	Ease	kJ/Cal expended
							Total:

THURSDAY

	Exercise	Time	Distance/resistance	Intensity	Heart rate	Ease	kJ/Cal expended
							Total:

FRIDAY

	Exercise	Time	Distance/resistance	Intensity	Heart rate	Ease	kJ/Cal expended
							Total:

SATURDAY

	Exercise	Time	Distance/resistance	Intensity	Heart rate	Ease	kJ/Cal expended
							Total:

SUNDAY

	Exercise	Time	Distance/resistance	Intensity	Heart rate	Ease	kJ/Cal expended
							Total:

Weekly Total:

Food Diary

MONDAY		kJ/Cal	Fat	Protein	Carbs
Breakfast Time: am/pm					
Lunch Time: am/pm					
Dinner Time: am/pm					
Snacks:					
Coffees/teas:	**Fluid intake:**	**Totals:**			

TUESDAY		kJ/Cal	Fat	Protein	Carbs
Breakfast Time: am/pm					
Lunch Time: am/pm					
Dinner Time: am/pm					
Snacks:					
Coffees/teas:	**Fluid intake:**	**Totals:**			

WEDNESDAY		kJ/Cal	Fat	Protein	Carbs
Breakfast Time: am/pm					
Lunch Time: am/pm					
Dinner Time: am/pm					
Snacks:					
Coffees/teas:	**Fluid intake:**	**Totals:**			

THURSDAY		kJ/Cal	Fat	Protein	Carbs
Breakfast Time: am/pm					
Lunch Time: am/pm					
Dinner Time: am/pm					
Snacks:					
Coffees/teas:	**Fluid intake:**	**Totals:**			

FRIDAY			kJ/Cal	Fat	Protein	Carbs
Breakfast Time: am/pm						
Lunch Time: am/pm						
Dinner Time: am/pm						
Snacks:						
Coffees/teas:	Fluid intake:	Totals:				

SATURDAY			kJ/Cal	Fat	Protein	Carbs
Breakfast Time: am/pm						
Lunch Time: am/pm						
Dinner Time: am/pm						
Snacks:						
Coffees/teas:	Fluid intake:	Totals:				

SUNDAY			kJ/Cal	Fat	Protein	Carbs
Breakfast Time: am/pm						
Lunch Time: am/pm						
Dinner Time: am/pm						
Snacks:						
Coffees/teas:	Fluid intake:	Totals:				

Units of alcohol this week: [　　　]   Total alcohol kJ/Cal: [　　　]

Vitamins and supplements

Weekly Totals	kJ/Cal	Fat	Protein	Carbs

Weekly Personal Summary

Energy level [1–5] [　]   Stress level [1–5] [　]

Hours of sleep [　]   Sleep quality [1–5] [　]

Mood [1–5] [　]   Appetite [1–5] [　]

kJ/Cal intake

Planned kJ/Cal	
Actual kJ/Cal	
Difference [+/-]	

Weight at start of week [　]

Weight at end of week [　]

BMI at start of week [　]

BMI at end of week [　]

Injuries or illnesses [　　　　　　　　　　　　]

Week Beginning

[ ] / [ ] / [ ]

Planned exercise sessions this week

	Exercise	Completed [Y/N]
Monday		
Tuesday		
Wednesday		
Thursday		
Friday		
Saturday		
Sunday		

Strength Training

MONDAY

Focus area	Equipment	SET 1		SET 2		SET 3		SET 4	
		Weight	Reps	Weight	Reps	Weight	Reps	Weight	Reps

TUESDAY

Focus area	Equipment	SET 1		SET 2		SET 3		SET 4	
		Weight	Reps	Weight	Reps	Weight	Reps	Weight	Reps

WEDNESDAY

Focus area	Equipment	SET 1		SET 2		SET 3		SET 4	
		Weight	Reps	Weight	Reps	Weight	Reps	Weight	Reps

THURSDAY

Focus area	Equipment	SET 1		SET 2		SET 3		SET 4	
		Weight	Reps	Weight	Reps	Weight	Reps	Weight	Reps

FRIDAY

Focus area	Equipment	SET 1		SET 2		SET 3		SET 4	
		Weight	Reps	Weight	Reps	Weight	Reps	Weight	Reps

SATURDAY

Focus area	Equipment	SET 1		SET 2		SET 3		SET 4	
		Weight	Reps	Weight	Reps	Weight	Reps	Weight	Reps

SUNDAY

Focus area	Equipment	SET 1		SET 2		SET 3		SET 4	
		Weight	Reps	Weight	Reps	Weight	Reps	Weight	Reps

Cardio Training

MONDAY	Exercise	Time	Distance/resistance	Intensity	Heart rate	Ease	kJ/Cal expended
							Total:

TUESDAY	Exercise	Time	Distance/resistance	Intensity	Heart rate	Ease	kJ/Cal expended
							Total:

WEDNESDAY	Exercise	Time	Distance/resistance	Intensity	Heart rate	Ease	kJ/Cal expended
							Total:

THURSDAY	Exercise	Time	Distance/resistance	Intensity	Heart rate	Ease	kJ/Cal expended
							Total:

FRIDAY	Exercise	Time	Distance/resistance	Intensity	Heart rate	Ease	kJ/Cal expended
							Total:

SATURDAY	Exercise	Time	Distance/resistance	Intensity	Heart rate	Ease	kJ/Cal expended
							Total:

SUNDAY	Exercise	Time	Distance/resistance	Intensity	Heart rate	Ease	kJ/Cal expended
							Total:

Weekly Total:

Food Diary

MONDAY		kJ/Cal	Fat	Protein	Carbs
Breakfast Time: am/pm					
Lunch Time: am/pm					
Dinner Time: am/pm					
Snacks:					
Coffees/teas:	**Fluid intake:**	**Totals:**			

TUESDAY		kJ/Cal	Fat	Protein	Carbs
Breakfast Time: am/pm					
Lunch Time: am/pm					
Dinner Time: am/pm					
Snacks:					
Coffees/teas:	**Fluid intake:**	**Totals:**			

WEDNESDAY		kJ/Cal	Fat	Protein	Carbs
Breakfast Time: am/pm					
Lunch Time: am/pm					
Dinner Time: am/pm					
Snacks:					
Coffees/teas:	**Fluid intake:**	**Totals:**			

THURSDAY		kJ/Cal	Fat	Protein	Carbs
Breakfast Time: am/pm					
Lunch Time: am/pm					
Dinner Time: am/pm					
Snacks:					
Coffees/teas:	**Fluid intake:**	**Totals:**			

FRIDAY			kJ/Cal	Fat	Protein	Carbs
Breakfast Time: am/pm						
Lunch Time: am/pm						
Dinner Time: am/pm						
Snacks:						
Coffees/teas:	Fluid intake:	Totals:				

SATURDAY			kJ/Cal	Fat	Protein	Carbs
Breakfast Time: am/pm						
Lunch Time: am/pm						
Dinner Time: am/pm						
Snacks:						
Coffees/teas:	Fluid intake:	Totals:				

SUNDAY			kJ/Cal	Fat	Protein	Carbs
Breakfast Time: am/pm						
Lunch Time: am/pm						
Dinner Time: am/pm						
Snacks:						
Coffees/teas:	Fluid intake:	Totals:				

Units of alcohol this week: Total alcohol kJ/Cal:

Vitamins and supplements

Weekly Totals	kJ/Cal	Fat	Protein	Carbs

Weekly Personal Summary

Energy level [1–5]

Stress level [1–5]

kJ/Cal intake

Planned kJ/Cal	
Actual kJ/Cal	

Difference [+/-]

Hours of sleep

Sleep quality [1–5]

Mood [1–5]

Appetite [1–5]

Weight at start of week

Weight at end of week

BMI at start of week

BMI at end of week

Injuries or illnesses

Week Beginning

[/ /]

Planned exercise sessions this week

	Exercise	Completed [Y/N]
Monday		
Tuesday		
Wednesday		
Thursday		
Friday		
Saturday		
Sunday		

Strength Training

MONDAY

Focus area	Equipment	SET 1		SET 2		SET 3		SET 4	
		Weight	Reps	Weight	Reps	Weight	Reps	Weight	Reps

TUESDAY

Focus area	Equipment	SET 1		SET 2		SET 3		SET 4	
		Weight	Reps	Weight	Reps	Weight	Reps	Weight	Reps

WEDNESDAY

Focus area	Equipment	SET 1		SET 2		SET 3		SET 4	
		Weight	Reps	Weight	Reps	Weight	Reps	Weight	Reps

THURSDAY

Focus area	Equipment	SET 1		SET 2		SET 3		SET 4	
		Weight	Reps	Weight	Reps	Weight	Reps	Weight	Reps

FRIDAY

Focus area	Equipment	SET 1		SET 2		SET 3		SET 4	
		Weight	Reps	Weight	Reps	Weight	Reps	Weight	Reps

SATURDAY

Focus area	Equipment	SET 1		SET 2		SET 3		SET 4	
		Weight	Reps	Weight	Reps	Weight	Reps	Weight	Reps

SUNDAY

Focus area	Equipment	SET 1		SET 2		SET 3		SET 4	
		Weight	Reps	Weight	Reps	Weight	Reps	Weight	Reps

Cardio Training

	Exercise	Time	Distance/resistance	Intensity	Heart rate	Ease	kJ/Cal expended
MONDAY							
							Total:

	Exercise	Time	Distance/resistance	Intensity	Heart rate	Ease	kJ/Cal expended
TUESDAY							
							Total:

	Exercise	Time	Distance/resistance	Intensity	Heart rate	Ease	kJ/Cal expended
WEDNESDAY							
							Total:

	Exercise	Time	Distance/resistance	Intensity	Heart rate	Ease	kJ/Cal expended
THURSDAY							
							Total:

	Exercise	Time	Distance/resistance	Intensity	Heart rate	Ease	kJ/Cal expended
FRIDAY							
							Total:

	Exercise	Time	Distance/resistance	Intensity	Heart rate	Ease	kJ/Cal expended
SATURDAY							
							Total:

	Exercise	Time	Distance/resistance	Intensity	Heart rate	Ease	kJ/Cal expended
SUNDAY							
							Total:
							Weekly Total:

Food Diary

MONDAY		kJ/Cal	Fat	Protein	Carbs
Breakfast Time: am/pm					
Lunch Time: am/pm					
Dinner Time: am/pm					
Snacks:					
Coffees/teas:	**Fluid intake:**	**Totals:**			

TUESDAY		kJ/Cal	Fat	Protein	Carbs
Breakfast Time: am/pm					
Lunch Time: am/pm					
Dinner Time: am/pm					
Snacks:					
Coffees/teas:	**Fluid intake:**	**Totals:**			

WEDNESDAY		kJ/Cal	Fat	Protein	Carbs
Breakfast Time: am/pm					
Lunch Time: am/pm					
Dinner Time: am/pm					
Snacks:					
Coffees/teas:	**Fluid intake:**	**Totals:**			

THURSDAY		kJ/Cal	Fat	Protein	Carbs
Breakfast Time: am/pm					
Lunch Time: am/pm					
Dinner Time: am/pm					
Snacks:					
Coffees/teas:	**Fluid intake:**	**Totals:**			

FRIDAY			kJ/Cal	Fat	Protein	Carbs
Breakfast Time: am/pm						
Lunch Time: am/pm						
Dinner Time: am/pm						
Snacks:						
Coffees/teas:	Fluid intake:	Totals:				

SATURDAY			kJ/Cal	Fat	Protein	Carbs
Breakfast Time: am/pm						
Lunch Time: am/pm						
Dinner Time: am/pm						
Snacks:						
Coffees/teas:	Fluid intake:	Totals:				

SUNDAY			kJ/Cal	Fat	Protein	Carbs
Breakfast Time: am/pm						
Lunch Time: am/pm						
Dinner Time: am/pm						
Snacks:						
Coffees/teas:	Fluid intake:	Totals:				

Units of alcohol this week: [ ]   Total alcohol kJ/Cal: [ ]

Vitamins and supplements

Weekly Totals	kJ/Cal	Fat	Protein	Carbs

Weekly Personal Summary

Energy level [1–5] [ ]   Stress level [1–5] [ ]

Hours of sleep [ ]   Sleep quality [1–5] [ ]

Mood [1–5] [ ]   Appetite [1–5] [ ]

kJ/Cal intake
Planned kJ/Cal [ ]
Actual kJ/Cal [ ]
Difference [+/-] [ ]

Weight at start of week [ ]
Weight at end of week [ ]
BMI at start of week [ ]
BMI at end of week [ ]

Injuries or illnesses [ ]

Week Beginning

[ ] / [ ] / [ ]

Planned exercise sessions this week

	Exercise	Completed [Y/N]
Monday		
Tuesday		
Wednesday		
Thursday		
Friday		
Saturday		
Sunday		

Strength Training

MONDAY

Focus area	Equipment	SET 1		SET 2		SET 3		SET 4	
		Weight	Reps	Weight	Reps	Weight	Reps	Weight	Reps

TUESDAY

Focus area	Equipment	SET 1		SET 2		SET 3		SET 4	
		Weight	Reps	Weight	Reps	Weight	Reps	Weight	Reps

WEDNESDAY

Focus area	Equipment	SET 1		SET 2		SET 3		SET 4	
		Weight	Reps	Weight	Reps	Weight	Reps	Weight	Reps

THURSDAY

Focus area	Equipment	SET 1		SET 2		SET 3		SET 4	
		Weight	Reps	Weight	Reps	Weight	Reps	Weight	Reps

FRIDAY

Focus area	Equipment	SET 1		SET 2		SET 3		SET 4	
		Weight	Reps	Weight	Reps	Weight	Reps	Weight	Reps

SATURDAY

Focus area	Equipment	SET 1		SET 2		SET 3		SET 4	
		Weight	Reps	Weight	Reps	Weight	Reps	Weight	Reps

SUNDAY

Focus area	Equipment	SET 1		SET 2		SET 3		SET 4	
		Weight	Reps	Weight	Reps	Weight	Reps	Weight	Reps

Cardio Training

	Exercise	Time	Distance/resistance	Intensity	Heart rate	Ease	kJ/Cal expended
MONDAY							
							Total:

	Exercise	Time	Distance/resistance	Intensity	Heart rate	Ease	kJ/Cal expended
TUESDAY							
							Total:

	Exercise	Time	Distance/resistance	Intensity	Heart rate	Ease	kJ/Cal expended
WEDNESDAY							
							Total:

	Exercise	Time	Distance/resistance	Intensity	Heart rate	Ease	kJ/Cal expended
THURSDAY							
							Total:

	Exercise	Time	Distance/resistance	Intensity	Heart rate	Ease	kJ/Cal expended
FRIDAY							
							Total:

	Exercise	Time	Distance/resistance	Intensity	Heart rate	Ease	kJ/Cal expended
SATURDAY							
							Total:

	Exercise	Time	Distance/resistance	Intensity	Heart rate	Ease	kJ/Cal expended
SUNDAY							
							Total:

Weekly Total:

Food Diary

MONDAY		kJ/Cal	Fat	Protein	Carbs
Breakfast Time: am/pm					
Lunch Time: am/pm					
Dinner Time: am/pm					
Snacks:					
Coffees/teas:	Fluid intake:	Totals:			

TUESDAY		kJ/Cal	Fat	Protein	Carbs
Breakfast Time: am/pm					
Lunch Time: am/pm					
Dinner Time: am/pm					
Snacks:					
Coffees/teas:	Fluid intake:	Totals:			

WEDNESDAY		kJ/Cal	Fat	Protein	Carbs
Breakfast Time: am/pm					
Lunch Time: am/pm					
Dinner Time: am/pm					
Snacks:					
Coffees/teas:	Fluid intake:	Totals:			

THURSDAY		kJ/Cal	Fat	Protein	Carbs
Breakfast Time: am/pm					
Lunch Time: am/pm					
Dinner Time: am/pm					
Snacks:					
Coffees/teas:	Fluid intake:	Totals:			

FRIDAY			kJ/Cal	Fat	Protein	Carbs
Breakfast Time: am/pm						
Lunch Time: am/pm						
Dinner Time: am/pm						
Snacks:						
Coffees/teas:	Fluid intake:	Totals:				

SATURDAY			kJ/Cal	Fat	Protein	Carbs
Breakfast Time: am/pm						
Lunch Time: am/pm						
Dinner Time: am/pm						
Snacks:						
Coffees/teas:	Fluid intake:	Totals:				

SUNDAY			kJ/Cal	Fat	Protein	Carbs
Breakfast Time: am/pm						
Lunch Time: am/pm						
Dinner Time: am/pm						
Snacks:						
Coffees/teas:	Fluid intake:	Totals:				

Units of alcohol this week: _____   Total alcohol kJ/Cal: _____

Vitamins and supplements

Weekly Totals	kJ/Cal	Fat	Protein	Carbs

Weekly Personal Summary

Energy level [1–5] ___   Stress level [1–5] ___

Hours of sleep ___   Sleep quality [1–5] ___

Mood [1–5] ___   Appetite [1–5] ___

kJ/Cal intake

Planned kJ/Cal	
Actual kJ/Cal	

Difference [+/-] _____

Weight at start of week ___
Weight at end of week ___
BMI at start of week ___
BMI at end of week ___

Injuries or illnesses _____

Week Beginning

[/ /]

Planned exercise sessions this week

	Exercise	Completed [Y/N]
Monday		
Tuesday		
Wednesday		
Thursday		
Friday		
Saturday		
Sunday		

Strength Training

MONDAY

Focus area	Equipment	SET 1		SET 2		SET 3		SET 4	
		Weight	Reps	Weight	Reps	Weight	Reps	Weight	Reps

TUESDAY

Focus area	Equipment	SET 1		SET 2		SET 3		SET 4	
		Weight	Reps	Weight	Reps	Weight	Reps	Weight	Reps

WEDNESDAY

Focus area	Equipment	SET 1		SET 2		SET 3		SET 4	
		Weight	Reps	Weight	Reps	Weight	Reps	Weight	Reps

THURSDAY

Focus area	Equipment	SET 1		SET 2		SET 3		SET 4	
		Weight	Reps	Weight	Reps	Weight	Reps	Weight	Reps

FRIDAY

Focus area	Equipment	SET 1		SET 2		SET 3		SET 4	
		Weight	Reps	Weight	Reps	Weight	Reps	Weight	Reps

SATURDAY

Focus area	Equipment	SET 1		SET 2		SET 3		SET 4	
		Weight	Reps	Weight	Reps	Weight	Reps	Weight	Reps

SUNDAY

Focus area	Equipment	SET 1		SET 2		SET 3		SET 4	
		Weight	Reps	Weight	Reps	Weight	Reps	Weight	Reps

Cardio Training

	Exercise	Time	Distance/resistance	Intensity	Heart rate	Ease	kJ/Cal expended
MONDAY							
							Total:

	Exercise	Time	Distance/resistance	Intensity	Heart rate	Ease	kJ/Cal expended
TUESDAY							
							Total:

	Exercise	Time	Distance/resistance	Intensity	Heart rate	Ease	kJ/Cal expended
WEDNESDAY							
							Total:

	Exercise	Time	Distance/resistance	Intensity	Heart rate	Ease	kJ/Cal expended
THURSDAY							
							Total:

	Exercise	Time	Distance/resistance	Intensity	Heart rate	Ease	kJ/Cal expended
FRIDAY							
							Total:

	Exercise	Time	Distance/resistance	Intensity	Heart rate	Ease	kJ/Cal expended
SATURDAY							
							Total:

	Exercise	Time	Distance/resistance	Intensity	Heart rate	Ease	kJ/Cal expended
SUNDAY							
							Total:

Weekly Total:

Food Diary

MONDAY		kJ/Cal	Fat	Protein	Carbs
Breakfast Time: am/pm					
Lunch Time: am/pm					
Dinner Time: am/pm					
Snacks:					
Coffees/teas:	Fluid intake:	Totals:			

TUESDAY		kJ/Cal	Fat	Protein	Carbs
Breakfast Time: am/pm					
Lunch Time: am/pm					
Dinner Time: am/pm					
Snacks:					
Coffees/teas:	Fluid intake:	Totals:			

WEDNESDAY		kJ/Cal	Fat	Protein	Carbs
Breakfast Time: am/pm					
Lunch Time: am/pm					
Dinner Time: am/pm					
Snacks:					
Coffees/teas:	Fluid intake:	Totals:			

THURSDAY		kJ/Cal	Fat	Protein	Carbs
Breakfast Time: am/pm					
Lunch Time: am/pm					
Dinner Time: am/pm					
Snacks:					
Coffees/teas:	Fluid intake:	Totals:			

FRIDAY		kJ/Cal	Fat	Protein	Carbs
Breakfast Time: am/pm					
Lunch Time: am/pm					
Dinner Time: am/pm					
Snacks:					
Coffees/teas:	Fluid intake: Totals:				

SATURDAY		kJ/Cal	Fat	Protein	Carbs
Breakfast Time: am/pm					
Lunch Time: am/pm					
Dinner Time: am/pm					
Snacks:					
Coffees/teas:	Fluid intake: Totals:				

SUNDAY		kJ/Cal	Fat	Protein	Carbs
Breakfast Time: am/pm					
Lunch Time: am/pm					
Dinner Time: am/pm					
Snacks:					
Coffees/teas:	Fluid intake: Totals:				

Units of alcohol this week: ____   Total alcohol kJ/Cal: ____

Vitamins and supplements

Weekly Totals	kJ/Cal	Fat	Protein	Carbs

Weekly Personal Summary

Energy level [1–5] ____   Stress level [1–5] ____

Hours of sleep ____   Sleep quality [1–5] ____

Mood [1–5] ____   Appetite [1–5] ____

kJ/Cal intake
Planned kJ/Cal	
Actual kJ/Cal	
Difference [+/-]	

Weight at start of week ____
Weight at end of week ____
BMI at start of week ____
BMI at end of week ____

Injuries or illnesses ____

Week Beginning

[   ] / [   ] / [   ]

	Exercise	Completed [Y/N]
Monday		
Tuesday		
Wednesday		
Thursday		
Friday		
Saturday		
Sunday		

Strength Training

MONDAY

Focus area	Equipment	SET 1 Weight	SET 1 Reps	SET 2 Weight	SET 2 Reps	SET 3 Weight	SET 3 Reps	SET 4 Weight	SET 4 Reps

TUESDAY

Focus area	Equipment	SET 1 Weight	SET 1 Reps	SET 2 Weight	SET 2 Reps	SET 3 Weight	SET 3 Reps	SET 4 Weight	SET 4 Reps

WEDNESDAY

Focus area	Equipment	SET 1 Weight	SET 1 Reps	SET 2 Weight	SET 2 Reps	SET 3 Weight	SET 3 Reps	SET 4 Weight	SET 4 Reps

THURSDAY

Focus area	Equipment	SET 1 Weight	SET 1 Reps	SET 2 Weight	SET 2 Reps	SET 3 Weight	SET 3 Reps	SET 4 Weight	SET 4 Reps

FRIDAY

Focus area	Equipment	SET 1 Weight	SET 1 Reps	SET 2 Weight	SET 2 Reps	SET 3 Weight	SET 3 Reps	SET 4 Weight	SET 4 Reps

SATURDAY

Focus area	Equipment	SET 1 Weight	SET 1 Reps	SET 2 Weight	SET 2 Reps	SET 3 Weight	SET 3 Reps	SET 4 Weight	SET 4 Reps

SUNDAY

Focus area	Equipment	SET 1 Weight	SET 1 Reps	SET 2 Weight	SET 2 Reps	SET 3 Weight	SET 3 Reps	SET 4 Weight	SET 4 Reps

Cardio Training

	Exercise	Time	Distance/resistance	Intensity	Heart rate	Ease	kJ/Cal expended
MONDAY							
							Total:

	Exercise	Time	Distance/resistance	Intensity	Heart rate	Ease	kJ/Cal expended
TUESDAY							
							Total:

	Exercise	Time	Distance/resistance	Intensity	Heart rate	Ease	kJ/Cal expended
WEDNESDAY							
							Total:

	Exercise	Time	Distance/resistance	Intensity	Heart rate	Ease	kJ/Cal expended
THURSDAY							
							Total:

	Exercise	Time	Distance/resistance	Intensity	Heart rate	Ease	kJ/Cal expended
FRIDAY							
							Total:

	Exercise	Time	Distance/resistance	Intensity	Heart rate	Ease	kJ/Cal expended
SATURDAY							
							Total:

	Exercise	Time	Distance/resistance	Intensity	Heart rate	Ease	kJ/Cal expended
SUNDAY							
							Total:

Weekly Total:

Food Diary

MONDAY		kJ/Cal	Fat	Protein	Carbs
Breakfast **Time:** am/pm					
Lunch **Time:** am/pm					
Dinner **Time:** am/pm					
Snacks:					
Coffees/teas:	Fluid intake:	Totals:			

TUESDAY		kJ/Cal	Fat	Protein	Carbs
Breakfast **Time:** am/pm					
Lunch **Time:** am/pm					
Dinner **Time:** am/pm					
Snacks:					
Coffees/teas:	Fluid intake:	Totals:			

WEDNESDAY		kJ/Cal	Fat	Protein	Carbs
Breakfast **Time:** am/pm					
Lunch **Time:** am/pm					
Dinner **Time:** am/pm					
Snacks:					
Coffees/teas:	Fluid intake:	Totals:			

THURSDAY		kJ/Cal	Fat	Protein	Carbs
Breakfast **Time:** am/pm					
Lunch **Time:** am/pm					
Dinner **Time:** am/pm					
Snacks:					
Coffees/teas:	Fluid intake:	Totals:			

FRIDAY		kJ/Cal	Fat	Protein	Carbs
Breakfast Time: am/pm					
Lunch Time: am/pm					
Dinner Time: am/pm					
Snacks:					
Coffees/teas:	Fluid intake:	Totals:			

SATURDAY		kJ/Cal	Fat	Protein	Carbs
Breakfast Time: am/pm					
Lunch Time: am/pm					
Dinner Time: am/pm					
Snacks:					
Coffees/teas:	Fluid intake:	Totals:			

SUNDAY		kJ/Cal	Fat	Protein	Carbs
Breakfast Time: am/pm					
Lunch Time: am/pm					
Dinner Time: am/pm					
Snacks:					
Coffees/teas:	Fluid intake:	Totals:			

Units of alcohol this week: Total alcohol kJ/Cal:

Vitamins and supplements

Weekly Totals	kJ/Cal	Fat	Protein	Carbs

Weekly Personal Summary

Energy level [1–5]   Stress level [1–5]

Hours of sleep   Sleep quality [1–5]

Mood [1–5]   Appetite [1–5]

kJ/Cal intake

| Planned kJ/Cal | |
| Actual kJ/Cal | |

Difference [+/-]

Weight at start of week

Weight at end of week

BMI at start of week

BMI at end of week

Injuries or illnesses

Week Beginning

| | | / | / | |

Planned exercise sessions this week

	Exercise	Completed [Y/N]
Monday		
Tuesday		
Wednesday		
Thursday		
Friday		
Saturday		
Sunday		

Strength Training

MONDAY

Focus area	Equipment	SET 1		SET 2		SET 3		SET 4	
		Weight	Reps	Weight	Reps	Weight	Reps	Weight	Reps

TUESDAY

Focus area	Equipment	SET 1		SET 2		SET 3		SET 4	
		Weight	Reps	Weight	Reps	Weight	Reps	Weight	Reps

WEDNESDAY

Focus area	Equipment	SET 1		SET 2		SET 3		SET 4	
		Weight	Reps	Weight	Reps	Weight	Reps	Weight	Reps

THURSDAY

Focus area	Equipment	SET 1		SET 2		SET 3		SET 4	
		Weight	Reps	Weight	Reps	Weight	Reps	Weight	Reps

FRIDAY

Focus area	Equipment	SET 1		SET 2		SET 3		SET 4	
		Weight	Reps	Weight	Reps	Weight	Reps	Weight	Reps

SATURDAY

Focus area	Equipment	SET 1		SET 2		SET 3		SET 4	
		Weight	Reps	Weight	Reps	Weight	Reps	Weight	Reps

SUNDAY

Focus area	Equipment	SET 1		SET 2		SET 3		SET 4	
		Weight	Reps	Weight	Reps	Weight	Reps	Weight	Reps

Cardio Training

	Exercise	Time	Distance/resistance	Intensity	Heart rate	Ease	kJ/Cal expended
MONDAY							
							Total:

	Exercise	Time	Distance/resistance	Intensity	Heart rate	Ease	kJ/Cal expended
TUESDAY							
							Total:

	Exercise	Time	Distance/resistance	Intensity	Heart rate	Ease	kJ/Cal expended
WEDNESDAY							
							Total:

	Exercise	Time	Distance/resistance	Intensity	Heart rate	Ease	kJ/Cal expended
THURSDAY							
							Total:

	Exercise	Time	Distance/resistance	Intensity	Heart rate	Ease	kJ/Cal expended
FRIDAY							
							Total:

	Exercise	Time	Distance/resistance	Intensity	Heart rate	Ease	kJ/Cal expended
SATURDAY							
							Total:

	Exercise	Time	Distance/resistance	Intensity	Heart rate	Ease	kJ/Cal expended
SUNDAY							
							Total:

Weekly Total:

Food Diary

MONDAY		kJ/Cal	Fat	Protein	Carbs
Breakfast Time: am/pm					
Lunch Time: am/pm					
Dinner Time: am/pm					
Snacks:					
Coffees/teas:	**Fluid intake:**	**Totals:**			

TUESDAY		kJ/Cal	Fat	Protein	Carbs
Breakfast Time: am/pm					
Lunch Time: am/pm					
Dinner Time: am/pm					
Snacks:					
Coffees/teas:	**Fluid intake:**	**Totals:**			

WEDNESDAY		kJ/Cal	Fat	Protein	Carbs
Breakfast Time: am/pm					
Lunch Time: am/pm					
Dinner Time: am/pm					
Snacks:					
Coffees/teas:	**Fluid intake:**	**Totals:**			

THURSDAY		kJ/Cal	Fat	Protein	Carbs
Breakfast Time: am/pm					
Lunch Time: am/pm					
Dinner Time: am/pm					
Snacks:					
Coffees/teas:	**Fluid intake:**	**Totals:**			

FRIDAY			kJ/Cal	Fat	Protein	Carbs
Breakfast Time: am/pm						
Lunch Time: am/pm						
Dinner Time: am/pm						
Snacks:						
Coffees/teas:	Fluid intake:	Totals:				

SATURDAY			kJ/Cal	Fat	Protein	Carbs
Breakfast Time: am/pm						
Lunch Time: am/pm						
Dinner Time: am/pm						
Snacks:						
Coffees/teas:	Fluid intake:	Totals:				

SUNDAY			kJ/Cal	Fat	Protein	Carbs
Breakfast Time: am/pm						
Lunch Time: am/pm						
Dinner Time: am/pm						
Snacks:						
Coffees/teas:	Fluid intake:	Totals:				

Units of alcohol this week: ☐   Total alcohol kJ/Cal: ☐

Vitamins and supplements

Weekly Totals	kJ/Cal	Fat	Protein	Carbs

Weekly Personal Summary

Energy level [1–5] ☐   Stress level [1–5] ☐

kJ/Cal intake

| Planned kJ/Cal | |
| Actual kJ/Cal | |
Difference [+/-] ☐

Hours of sleep ☐   Sleep quality [1–5] ☐

Mood [1–5] ☐   Appetite [1–5] ☐

Weight at start of week ☐
Weight at end of week ☐
BMI at start of week ☐
BMI at end of week ☐

Injuries or illnesses ☐

Week Beginning

Planned exercise sessions this week

	Exercise	Completed [Y/N]
Monday		
Tuesday		
Wednesday		
Thursday		
Friday		
Saturday		
Sunday		

Strength Training

MONDAY

Focus area	Equipment	SET 1		SET 2		SET 3		SET 4	
		Weight	Reps	Weight	Reps	Weight	Reps	Weight	Reps

TUESDAY

Focus area	Equipment	SET 1		SET 2		SET 3		SET 4	
		Weight	Reps	Weight	Reps	Weight	Reps	Weight	Reps

WEDNESDAY

Focus area	Equipment	SET 1		SET 2		SET 3		SET 4	
		Weight	Reps	Weight	Reps	Weight	Reps	Weight	Reps

THURSDAY

Focus area	Equipment	SET 1		SET 2		SET 3		SET 4	
		Weight	Reps	Weight	Reps	Weight	Reps	Weight	Reps

FRIDAY

Focus area	Equipment	SET 1		SET 2		SET 3		SET 4	
		Weight	Reps	Weight	Reps	Weight	Reps	Weight	Reps

SATURDAY

Focus area	Equipment	SET 1		SET 2		SET 3		SET 4	
		Weight	Reps	Weight	Reps	Weight	Reps	Weight	Reps

SUNDAY

Focus area	Equipment	SET 1		SET 2		SET 3		SET 4	
		Weight	Reps	Weight	Reps	Weight	Reps	Weight	Reps

Cardio Training

	Exercise	Time	Distance/resistance	Intensity	Heart rate	Ease	kJ/Cal expended
MONDAY							
							Total:

	Exercise	Time	Distance/resistance	Intensity	Heart rate	Ease	kJ/Cal expended
TUESDAY							
							Total:

	Exercise	Time	Distance/resistance	Intensity	Heart rate	Ease	kJ/Cal expended
WEDNESDAY							
							Total:

	Exercise	Time	Distance/resistance	Intensity	Heart rate	Ease	kJ/Cal expended
THURSDAY							
							Total:

	Exercise	Time	Distance/resistance	Intensity	Heart rate	Ease	kJ/Cal expended
FRIDAY							
							Total:

	Exercise	Time	Distance/resistance	Intensity	Heart rate	Ease	kJ/Cal expended
SATURDAY							
							Total:

	Exercise	Time	Distance/resistance	Intensity	Heart rate	Ease	kJ/Cal expended
SUNDAY							
							Total:

Weekly Total:

Food Diary

MONDAY		kJ/Cal	Fat	Protein	Carbs
Breakfast Time: am/pm					
Lunch Time: am/pm					
Dinner Time: am/pm					
Snacks:					
Coffees/teas:	Fluid intake:	Totals:			

TUESDAY		kJ/Cal	Fat	Protein	Carbs
Breakfast Time: am/pm					
Lunch Time: am/pm					
Dinner Time: am/pm					
Snacks:					
Coffees/teas:	Fluid intake:	Totals:			

WEDNESDAY		kJ/Cal	Fat	Protein	Carbs
Breakfast Time: am/pm					
Lunch Time: am/pm					
Dinner Time: am/pm					
Snacks:					
Coffees/teas:	Fluid intake:	Totals:			

THURSDAY		kJ/Cal	Fat	Protein	Carbs
Breakfast Time: am/pm					
Lunch Time: am/pm					
Dinner Time: am/pm					
Snacks:					
Coffees/teas:	Fluid intake:	Totals:			

FRIDAY		kJ/Cal	Fat	Protein	Carbs
Breakfast Time: am/pm					
Lunch Time: am/pm					
Dinner Time: am/pm					
Snacks:					
Coffees/teas:	Fluid intake:	Totals:			

SATURDAY		kJ/Cal	Fat	Protein	Carbs
Breakfast Time: am/pm					
Lunch Time: am/pm					
Dinner Time: am/pm					
Snacks:					
Coffees/teas:	Fluid intake:	Totals:			

SUNDAY		kJ/Cal	Fat	Protein	Carbs
Breakfast Time: am/pm					
Lunch Time: am/pm					
Dinner Time: am/pm					
Snacks:					
Coffees/teas:	Fluid intake:	Totals:			

Units of alcohol this week: [ ]   Total alcohol kJ/Cal: [ ]

Vitamins and supplements

Weekly Totals	kJ/Cal	Fat	Protein	Carbs

Weekly Personal Summary

Energy level 1–5 [ ]   Stress level 1–5 [ ]

Hours of sleep [ ]   Sleep quality 1–5 [ ]

Mood 1–5 [ ]   Appetite 1–5 [ ]

kJ/Cal intake

Planned kJ/Cal	
Actual kJ/Cal	
Difference [+/-]	

Weight at start of week [ ]

Weight at end of week [ ]

BMI at start of week [ ]

BMI at end of week [ ]

Injuries or illnesses [ ]

105

Week Beginning

| / / |

Planned exercise sessions this week

	Exercise	Completed [Y/N]
Monday		
Tuesday		
Wednesday		
Thursday		
Friday		
Saturday		
Sunday		

Strength Training

MONDAY

Focus area	Equipment	SET 1		SET 2		SET 3		SET 4	
		Weight	Reps	Weight	Reps	Weight	Reps	Weight	Reps

TUESDAY

Focus area	Equipment	SET 1		SET 2		SET 3		SET 4	
		Weight	Reps	Weight	Reps	Weight	Reps	Weight	Reps

WEDNESDAY

Focus area	Equipment	SET 1		SET 2		SET 3		SET 4	
		Weight	Reps	Weight	Reps	Weight	Reps	Weight	Reps

THURSDAY

Focus area	Equipment	SET 1		SET 2		SET 3		SET 4	
		Weight	Reps	Weight	Reps	Weight	Reps	Weight	Reps

FRIDAY

Focus area	Equipment	SET 1		SET 2		SET 3		SET 4	
		Weight	Reps	Weight	Reps	Weight	Reps	Weight	Reps

SATURDAY

Focus area	Equipment	SET 1		SET 2		SET 3		SET 4	
		Weight	Reps	Weight	Reps	Weight	Reps	Weight	Reps

SUNDAY

Focus area	Equipment	SET 1		SET 2		SET 3		SET 4	
		Weight	Reps	Weight	Reps	Weight	Reps	Weight	Reps

Cardio Training

MONDAY	Exercise	Time	Distance/resistance	Intensity	Heart rate	Ease	kJ/Cal expended
							Total:

TUESDAY	Exercise	Time	Distance/resistance	Intensity	Heart rate	Ease	kJ/Cal expended
							Total:

WEDNESDAY	Exercise	Time	Distance/resistance	Intensity	Heart rate	Ease	kJ/Cal expended
							Total:

THURSDAY	Exercise	Time	Distance/resistance	Intensity	Heart rate	Ease	kJ/Cal expended
							Total:

FRIDAY	Exercise	Time	Distance/resistance	Intensity	Heart rate	Ease	kJ/Cal expended
							Total:

SATURDAY	Exercise	Time	Distance/resistance	Intensity	Heart rate	Ease	kJ/Cal expended
							Total:

SUNDAY	Exercise	Time	Distance/resistance	Intensity	Heart rate	Ease	kJ/Cal expended
							Total:

Weekly Total:

Food Diary

MONDAY		kJ/Cal	Fat	Protein	Carbs
Breakfast Time: am/pm					
Lunch Time: am/pm					
Dinner Time: am/pm					
Snacks:					
Coffees/teas:	Fluid intake:	Totals:			

TUESDAY		kJ/Cal	Fat	Protein	Carbs
Breakfast Time: am/pm					
Lunch Time: am/pm					
Dinner Time: am/pm					
Snacks:					
Coffees/teas:	Fluid intake:	Totals:			

WEDNESDAY		kJ/Cal	Fat	Protein	Carbs
Breakfast Time: am/pm					
Lunch Time: am/pm					
Dinner Time: am/pm					
Snacks:					
Coffees/teas:	Fluid intake:	Totals:			

THURSDAY		kJ/Cal	Fat	Protein	Carbs
Breakfast Time: am/pm					
Lunch Time: am/pm					
Dinner Time: am/pm					
Snacks:					
Coffees/teas:	Fluid intake:	Totals:			

FRIDAY		kJ/Cal	Fat	Protein	Carbs
Breakfast Time: am/pm					
Lunch Time: am/pm					
Dinner Time: am/pm					
Snacks:					
Coffees/teas:	Fluid intake:	Totals:			

SATURDAY		kJ/Cal	Fat	Protein	Carbs
Breakfast Time: am/pm					
Lunch Time: am/pm					
Dinner Time: am/pm					
Snacks:					
Coffees/teas:	Fluid intake:	Totals:			

SUNDAY		kJ/Cal	Fat	Protein	Carbs
Breakfast Time: am/pm					
Lunch Time: am/pm					
Dinner Time: am/pm					
Snacks:					
Coffees/teas:	Fluid intake:	Totals:			

Units of alcohol this week: Total alcohol kJ/Cal:

Vitamins and supplements

Weekly Totals	kJ/Cal	Fat	Protein	Carbs

Weekly Personal Summary

Energy level 1–5

Stress level 1–5

Hours of sleep

Sleep quality 1–5

Mood 1–5

Appetite 1–5

kJ/Cal intake

Planned kJ/Cal	
Actual kJ/Cal	
Difference [+/-]	

Weight at start of week

Weight at end of week

BMI at start of week

BMI at end of week

Injuries or illnesses

Week Beginning

[ ] / [ ] / [ ]

Planned exercise sessions this week

	Exercise	Completed [Y/N]
Monday		
Tuesday		
Wednesday		
Thursday		
Friday		
Saturday		
Sunday		

Strength Training

MONDAY

Focus area	Equipment	SET 1		SET 2		SET 3		SET 4	
		Weight	Reps	Weight	Reps	Weight	Reps	Weight	Reps

TUESDAY

Focus area	Equipment	SET 1		SET 2		SET 3		SET 4	
		Weight	Reps	Weight	Reps	Weight	Reps	Weight	Reps

WEDNESDAY

Focus area	Equipment	SET 1		SET 2		SET 3		SET 4	
		Weight	Reps	Weight	Reps	Weight	Reps	Weight	Reps

THURSDAY

Focus area	Equipment	SET 1		SET 2		SET 3		SET 4	
		Weight	Reps	Weight	Reps	Weight	Reps	Weight	Reps

FRIDAY

Focus area	Equipment	SET 1		SET 2		SET 3		SET 4	
		Weight	Reps	Weight	Reps	Weight	Reps	Weight	Reps

SATURDAY

Focus area	Equipment	SET 1		SET 2		SET 3		SET 4	
		Weight	Reps	Weight	Reps	Weight	Reps	Weight	Reps

SUNDAY

Focus area	Equipment	SET 1		SET 2		SET 3		SET 4	
		Weight	Reps	Weight	Reps	Weight	Reps	Weight	Reps

Cardio Training

MONDAY

Exercise	Time	Distance/resistance	Intensity	Heart rate	Ease	kJ/Cal expended
						Total:

TUESDAY

Exercise	Time	Distance/resistance	Intensity	Heart rate	Ease	kJ/Cal expended
						Total:

WEDNESDAY

Exercise	Time	Distance/resistance	Intensity	Heart rate	Ease	kJ/Cal expended
						Total:

THURSDAY

Exercise	Time	Distance/resistance	Intensity	Heart rate	Ease	kJ/Cal expended
						Total:

FRIDAY

Exercise	Time	Distance/resistance	Intensity	Heart rate	Ease	kJ/Cal expended
						Total:

SATURDAY

Exercise	Time	Distance/resistance	Intensity	Heart rate	Ease	kJ/Cal expended
						Total:

SUNDAY

Exercise	Time	Distance/resistance	Intensity	Heart rate	Ease	kJ/Cal expended
						Total:

Weekly Total:

Food Diary

MONDAY		kJ/Cal	Fat	Protein	Carbs
Breakfast Time: am/pm					
Lunch Time: am/pm					
Dinner Time: am/pm					
Snacks:					
Coffees/teas:	Fluid intake:	Totals:			

TUESDAY		kJ/Cal	Fat	Protein	Carbs
Breakfast Time: am/pm					
Lunch Time: am/pm					
Dinner Time: am/pm					
Snacks:					
Coffees/teas:	Fluid intake:	Totals:			

WEDNESDAY		kJ/Cal	Fat	Protein	Carbs
Breakfast Time: am/pm					
Lunch Time: am/pm					
Dinner Time: am/pm					
Snacks:					
Coffees/teas:	Fluid intake:	Totals:			

THURSDAY		kJ/Cal	Fat	Protein	Carbs
Breakfast Time: am/pm					
Lunch Time: am/pm					
Dinner Time: am/pm					
Snacks:					
Coffees/teas:	Fluid intake:	Totals:			

FRIDAY		kJ/Cal	Fat	Protein	Carbs
Breakfast Time: am/pm					
Lunch Time: am/pm					
Dinner Time: am/pm					
Snacks:					
Coffees/teas:	Fluid intake:	Totals:			

SATURDAY		kJ/Cal	Fat	Protein	Carbs
Breakfast Time: am/pm					
Lunch Time: am/pm					
Dinner Time: am/pm					
Snacks:					
Coffees/teas:	Fluid intake:	Totals:			

SUNDAY		kJ/Cal	Fat	Protein	Carbs
Breakfast Time: am/pm					
Lunch Time: am/pm					
Dinner Time: am/pm					
Snacks:					
Coffees/teas:	Fluid intake:	Totals:			

Units of alcohol this week: [　　　]   Total alcohol kJ/Cal: [　　　]

Vitamins and supplements

Weekly Totals	kJ/Cal	Fat	Protein	Carbs

Weekly Personal Summary

Energy level [1–5]   Stress level [1–5]

Hours of sleep [　]   Sleep quality [1–5]

Mood [1–5]   Appetite [1–5]

kJ/Cal intake
Planned kJ/Cal [　　]
Actual kJ/Cal [　　]
Difference [+/-] [　　]

Weight at start of week [　]
Weight at end of week [　]
BMI at start of week [　]
BMI at end of week [　]

Injuries or illnesses [　　　　　　　　　　　　　　　]

Week Beginning

`/    /`

Planned exercise sessions this week

	Exercise	Completed [Y/N]
Monday		
Tuesday		
Wednesday		
Thursday		
Friday		
Saturday		
Sunday		

Strength Training

MONDAY

Focus area	Equipment	SET 1		SET 2		SET 3		SET 4	
		Weight	Reps	Weight	Reps	Weight	Reps	Weight	Reps

TUESDAY

Focus area	Equipment	SET 1		SET 2		SET 3		SET 4	
		Weight	Reps	Weight	Reps	Weight	Reps	Weight	Reps

WEDNESDAY

Focus area	Equipment	SET 1		SET 2		SET 3		SET 4	
		Weight	Reps	Weight	Reps	Weight	Reps	Weight	Reps

THURSDAY

Focus area	Equipment	SET 1		SET 2		SET 3		SET 4	
		Weight	Reps	Weight	Reps	Weight	Reps	Weight	Reps

FRIDAY

Focus area	Equipment	SET 1		SET 2		SET 3		SET 4	
		Weight	Reps	Weight	Reps	Weight	Reps	Weight	Reps

SATURDAY

Focus area	Equipment	SET 1		SET 2		SET 3		SET 4	
		Weight	Reps	Weight	Reps	Weight	Reps	Weight	Reps

SUNDAY

Focus area	Equipment	SET 1		SET 2		SET 3		SET 4	
		Weight	Reps	Weight	Reps	Weight	Reps	Weight	Reps

Cardio Training

MONDAY

Exercise	Time	Distance/resistance	Intensity	Heart rate	Ease	kJ/Cal expended
						Total:

TUESDAY

Exercise	Time	Distance/resistance	Intensity	Heart rate	Ease	kJ/Cal expended
						Total:

WEDNESDAY

Exercise	Time	Distance/resistance	Intensity	Heart rate	Ease	kJ/Cal expended
						Total:

THURSDAY

Exercise	Time	Distance/resistance	Intensity	Heart rate	Ease	kJ/Cal expended
						Total:

FRIDAY

Exercise	Time	Distance/resistance	Intensity	Heart rate	Ease	kJ/Cal expended
						Total:

SATURDAY

Exercise	Time	Distance/resistance	Intensity	Heart rate	Ease	kJ/Cal expended
						Total:

SUNDAY

Exercise	Time	Distance/resistance	Intensity	Heart rate	Ease	kJ/Cal expended
						Total:

Weekly Total:

Food Diary

MONDAY		kJ/Cal	Fat	Protein	Carbs
Breakfast Time: am/pm					
Lunch Time: am/pm					
Dinner Time: am/pm					
Snacks:					
Coffees/teas:	Fluid intake: **Totals:**				

TUESDAY		kJ/Cal	Fat	Protein	Carbs
Breakfast Time: am/pm					
Lunch Time: am/pm					
Dinner Time: am/pm					
Snacks:					
Coffees/teas:	Fluid intake: **Totals:**				

WEDNESDAY		kJ/Cal	Fat	Protein	Carbs
Breakfast Time: am/pm					
Lunch Time: am/pm					
Dinner Time: am/pm					
Snacks:					
Coffees/teas:	Fluid intake: **Totals:**				

THURSDAY		kJ/Cal	Fat	Protein	Carbs
Breakfast Time: am/pm					
Lunch Time: am/pm					
Dinner Time: am/pm					
Snacks:					
Coffees/teas:	Fluid intake: **Totals:**				

FRIDAY		kJ/Cal	Fat	Protein	Carbs
Breakfast Time: am/pm					
Lunch Time: am/pm					
Dinner Time: am/pm					
Snacks:					
Coffees/teas:	Fluid intake:	Totals:			

SATURDAY		kJ/Cal	Fat	Protein	Carbs
Breakfast Time: am/pm					
Lunch Time: am/pm					
Dinner Time: am/pm					
Snacks:					
Coffees/teas:	Fluid intake:	Totals:			

SUNDAY		kJ/Cal	Fat	Protein	Carbs
Breakfast Time: am/pm					
Lunch Time: am/pm					
Dinner Time: am/pm					
Snacks:					
Coffees/teas:	Fluid intake:	Totals:			

Units of alcohol this week: ☐   Total alcohol kJ/Cal: ☐

Vitamins and supplements

Weekly Totals	kJ/Cal	Fat	Protein	Carbs

Weekly Personal Summary

Energy level 1–5 ☐   Stress level 1–5 ☐

Hours of sleep ☐   Sleep quality 1–5 ☐

Mood 1–5 ☐   Appetite 1–5 ☐

kJ/Cal intake

Planned kJ/Cal	
Actual kJ/Cal	

Difference [+/-] ☐

Weight at start of week ☐

Weight at end of week ☐

BMI at start of week ☐

BMI at end of week ☐

Injuries or illnesses ☐

Week Beginning

[/   /   ]

Planned exercise sessions this week

	Exercise	Completed [Y/N]
Monday		
Tuesday		
Wednesday		
Thursday		
Friday		
Saturday		
Sunday		

Strength Training

MONDAY

Focus area	Equipment	SET 1		SET 2		SET 3		SET 4	
		Weight	Reps	Weight	Reps	Weight	Reps	Weight	Reps

TUESDAY

Focus area	Equipment	SET 1		SET 2		SET 3		SET 4	
		Weight	Reps	Weight	Reps	Weight	Reps	Weight	Reps

WEDNESDAY

Focus area	Equipment	SET 1		SET 2		SET 3		SET 4	
		Weight	Reps	Weight	Reps	Weight	Reps	Weight	Reps

THURSDAY

Focus area	Equipment	SET 1		SET 2		SET 3		SET 4	
		Weight	Reps	Weight	Reps	Weight	Reps	Weight	Reps

FRIDAY

Focus area	Equipment	SET 1		SET 2		SET 3		SET 4	
		Weight	Reps	Weight	Reps	Weight	Reps	Weight	Reps

SATURDAY

Focus area	Equipment	SET 1		SET 2		SET 3		SET 4	
		Weight	Reps	Weight	Reps	Weight	Reps	Weight	Reps

SUNDAY

Focus area	Equipment	SET 1		SET 2		SET 3		SET 4	
		Weight	Reps	Weight	Reps	Weight	Reps	Weight	Reps

Cardio Training

	Exercise	Time	Distance/resistance	Intensity	Heart rate	Ease	kJ/Cal expended
MONDAY							
							Total:

	Exercise	Time	Distance/resistance	Intensity	Heart rate	Ease	kJ/Cal expended
TUESDAY							
							Total:

	Exercise	Time	Distance/resistance	Intensity	Heart rate	Ease	kJ/Cal expended
WEDNESDAY							
							Total:

	Exercise	Time	Distance/resistance	Intensity	Heart rate	Ease	kJ/Cal expended
THURSDAY							
							Total:

	Exercise	Time	Distance/resistance	Intensity	Heart rate	Ease	kJ/Cal expended
FRIDAY							
							Total:

	Exercise	Time	Distance/resistance	Intensity	Heart rate	Ease	kJ/Cal expended
SATURDAY							
							Total:

	Exercise	Time	Distance/resistance	Intensity	Heart rate	Ease	kJ/Cal expended
SUNDAY							
							Total:

Weekly Total:

Food Diary

MONDAY		kJ/Cal	Fat	Protein	Carbs
Breakfast Time: am/pm					
Lunch Time: am/pm					
Dinner Time: am/pm					
Snacks:					
Coffees/teas:	Fluid intake:	Totals:			

TUESDAY		kJ/Cal	Fat	Protein	Carbs
Breakfast Time: am/pm					
Lunch Time: am/pm					
Dinner Time: am/pm					
Snacks:					
Coffees/teas:	Fluid intake:	Totals:			

WEDNESDAY		kJ/Cal	Fat	Protein	Carbs
Breakfast Time: am/pm					
Lunch Time: am/pm					
Dinner Time: am/pm					
Snacks:					
Coffees/teas:	Fluid intake:	Totals:			

THURSDAY		kJ/Cal	Fat	Protein	Carbs
Breakfast Time: am/pm					
Lunch Time: am/pm					
Dinner Time: am/pm					
Snacks:					
Coffees/teas:	Fluid intake:	Totals:			

FRIDAY			kJ/Cal	Fat	Protein	Carbs
Breakfast Time: am/pm						
Lunch Time: am/pm						
Dinner Time: am/pm						
Snacks:						
Coffees/teas:	Fluid intake:	Totals:				

SATURDAY			kJ/Cal	Fat	Protein	Carbs
Breakfast Time: am/pm						
Lunch Time: am/pm						
Dinner Time: am/pm						
Snacks:						
Coffees/teas:	Fluid intake:	Totals:				

SUNDAY			kJ/Cal	Fat	Protein	Carbs
Breakfast Time: am/pm						
Lunch Time: am/pm						
Dinner Time: am/pm						
Snacks:						
Coffees/teas:	Fluid intake:	Totals:				

Units of alcohol this week: [ ]   Total alcohol kJ/Cal: [ ]

Vitamins and supplements

Weekly Totals	kJ/Cal	Fat	Protein	Carbs

Weekly Personal Summary

Energy level   1-5 [ ]   Stress level   1-5 [ ]

Hours of sleep [ ]   Sleep quality   1-5 [ ]

Mood   1-5 [ ]   Appetite   1-5 [ ]

kJ/Cal intake

Planned kJ/Cal	[ ]
Actual kJ/Cal	[ ]
Difference [+/-]	[ ]

Weight at start of week [ ]
Weight at end of week [ ]
BMI at start of week [ ]
BMI at end of week [ ]

Injuries or illnesses [ ]

Week Beginning

__ / __ / __

Planned exercise sessions this week

	Exercise	Completed [Y/N]
Monday		
Tuesday		
Wednesday		
Thursday		
Friday		
Saturday		
Sunday		

Strength Training

MONDAY

Focus area	Equipment	SET 1 Weight	SET 1 Reps	SET 2 Weight	SET 2 Reps	SET 3 Weight	SET 3 Reps	SET 4 Weight	SET 4 Reps

TUESDAY

Focus area	Equipment	SET 1 Weight	SET 1 Reps	SET 2 Weight	SET 2 Reps	SET 3 Weight	SET 3 Reps	SET 4 Weight	SET 4 Reps

WEDNESDAY

Focus area	Equipment	SET 1 Weight	SET 1 Reps	SET 2 Weight	SET 2 Reps	SET 3 Weight	SET 3 Reps	SET 4 Weight	SET 4 Reps

THURSDAY

Focus area	Equipment	SET 1 Weight	SET 1 Reps	SET 2 Weight	SET 2 Reps	SET 3 Weight	SET 3 Reps	SET 4 Weight	SET 4 Reps

FRIDAY

Focus area	Equipment	SET 1 Weight	SET 1 Reps	SET 2 Weight	SET 2 Reps	SET 3 Weight	SET 3 Reps	SET 4 Weight	SET 4 Reps

SATURDAY

Focus area	Equipment	SET 1 Weight	SET 1 Reps	SET 2 Weight	SET 2 Reps	SET 3 Weight	SET 3 Reps	SET 4 Weight	SET 4 Reps

SUNDAY

Focus area	Equipment	SET 1 Weight	SET 1 Reps	SET 2 Weight	SET 2 Reps	SET 3 Weight	SET 3 Reps	SET 4 Weight	SET 4 Reps

Cardio Training

MONDAY

Exercise	Time	Distance/ resistance	Intensity	Heart rate	Ease	kJ/Cal expended
						Total:

TUESDAY

Exercise	Time	Distance/ resistance	Intensity	Heart rate	Ease	kJ/Cal expended
						Total:

WEDNESDAY

Exercise	Time	Distance/ resistance	Intensity	Heart rate	Ease	kJ/Cal expended
						Total:

THURSDAY

Exercise	Time	Distance/ resistance	Intensity	Heart rate	Ease	kJ/Cal expended
						Total:

FRIDAY

Exercise	Time	Distance/ resistance	Intensity	Heart rate	Ease	kJ/Cal expended
						Total:

SATURDAY

Exercise	Time	Distance/ resistance	Intensity	Heart rate	Ease	kJ/Cal expended
						Total:

SUNDAY

Exercise	Time	Distance/ resistance	Intensity	Heart rate	Ease	kJ/Cal expended
						Total:

Weekly Total:

Food Diary

MONDAY		kJ/Cal	Fat	Protein	Carbs
Breakfast Time: am/pm					
Lunch Time: am/pm					
Dinner Time: am/pm					
Snacks:					
Coffees/teas:	**Fluid intake:**	**Totals:**			

TUESDAY		kJ/Cal	Fat	Protein	Carbs
Breakfast Time: am/pm					
Lunch Time: am/pm					
Dinner Time: am/pm					
Snacks:					
Coffees/teas:	**Fluid intake:**	**Totals:**			

WEDNESDAY		kJ/Cal	Fat	Protein	Carbs
Breakfast Time: am/pm					
Lunch Time: am/pm					
Dinner Time: am/pm					
Snacks:					
Coffees/teas:	**Fluid intake:**	**Totals:**			

THURSDAY		kJ/Cal	Fat	Protein	Carbs
Breakfast Time: am/pm					
Lunch Time: am/pm					
Dinner Time: am/pm					
Snacks:					
Coffees/teas:	**Fluid intake:**	**Totals:**			

FRIDAY		kJ/Cal	Fat	Protein	Carbs
Breakfast Time: am/pm					
Lunch Time: am/pm					
Dinner Time: am/pm					
Snacks:					
Coffees/teas:	Fluid intake:	Totals:			

SATURDAY		kJ/Cal	Fat	Protein	Carbs
Breakfast Time: am/pm					
Lunch Time: am/pm					
Dinner Time: am/pm					
Snacks:					
Coffees/teas:	Fluid intake:	Totals:			

SUNDAY		kJ/Cal	Fat	Protein	Carbs
Breakfast Time: am/pm					
Lunch Time: am/pm					
Dinner Time: am/pm					
Snacks:					
Coffees/teas:	Fluid intake:	Totals:			

Units of alcohol this week: ☐   Total alcohol kJ/Cal: ☐

Vitamins and supplements

Weekly Totals	kJ/Cal	Fat	Protein	Carbs

Weekly Personal Summary

Energy level 1–5 ☐   Stress level 1–5 ☐

Hours of sleep ☐   Sleep quality 1–5 ☐

Mood 1–5 ☐   Appetite 1–5 ☐

kJ/Cal intake

Planned kJ/Cal	
Actual kJ/Cal	

Difference [+/-] ☐

Weight at start of week ☐

Weight at end of week ☐

BMI at start of week ☐

BMI at end of week ☐

Injuries or illnesses _____

125

Week Beginning

[ ] / [ ] / [ ]

Planned exercise sessions this week

	Exercise	Completed [Y/N]
Monday		
Tuesday		
Wednesday		
Thursday		
Friday		
Saturday		
Sunday		

Strength Training

MONDAY

Focus area	Equipment	SET 1 Weight	SET 1 Reps	SET 2 Weight	SET 2 Reps	SET 3 Weight	SET 3 Reps	SET 4 Weight	SET 4 Reps

TUESDAY

Focus area	Equipment	SET 1 Weight	SET 1 Reps	SET 2 Weight	SET 2 Reps	SET 3 Weight	SET 3 Reps	SET 4 Weight	SET 4 Reps

WEDNESDAY

Focus area	Equipment	SET 1 Weight	SET 1 Reps	SET 2 Weight	SET 2 Reps	SET 3 Weight	SET 3 Reps	SET 4 Weight	SET 4 Reps

THURSDAY

Focus area	Equipment	SET 1 Weight	SET 1 Reps	SET 2 Weight	SET 2 Reps	SET 3 Weight	SET 3 Reps	SET 4 Weight	SET 4 Reps

FRIDAY

Focus area	Equipment	SET 1 Weight	SET 1 Reps	SET 2 Weight	SET 2 Reps	SET 3 Weight	SET 3 Reps	SET 4 Weight	SET 4 Reps

SATURDAY

Focus area	Equipment	SET 1 Weight	SET 1 Reps	SET 2 Weight	SET 2 Reps	SET 3 Weight	SET 3 Reps	SET 4 Weight	SET 4 Reps

SUNDAY

Focus area	Equipment	SET 1 Weight	SET 1 Reps	SET 2 Weight	SET 2 Reps	SET 3 Weight	SET 3 Reps	SET 4 Weight	SET 4 Reps

Cardio Training

	Exercise	Time	Distance/resistance	Intensity	Heart rate	Ease	kJ/Cal expended
MONDAY							
							Total:

	Exercise	Time	Distance/resistance	Intensity	Heart rate	Ease	kJ/Cal expended
TUESDAY							
							Total:

	Exercise	Time	Distance/resistance	Intensity	Heart rate	Ease	kJ/Cal expended
WEDNESDAY							
							Total:

	Exercise	Time	Distance/resistance	Intensity	Heart rate	Ease	kJ/Cal expended
THURSDAY							
							Total:

	Exercise	Time	Distance/resistance	Intensity	Heart rate	Ease	kJ/Cal expended
FRIDAY							
							Total:

	Exercise	Time	Distance/resistance	Intensity	Heart rate	Ease	kJ/Cal expended
SATURDAY							
							Total:

	Exercise	Time	Distance/resistance	Intensity	Heart rate	Ease	kJ/Cal expended
SUNDAY							
							Total:
							Weekly Total:

Food Diary

MONDAY		kJ/Cal	Fat	Protein	Carbs
Breakfast Time: am/pm					
Lunch Time: am/pm					
Dinner Time: am/pm					
Snacks:					
Coffees/teas:	Fluid intake:	Totals:			

TUESDAY		kJ/Cal	Fat	Protein	Carbs
Breakfast Time: am/pm					
Lunch Time: am/pm					
Dinner Time: am/pm					
Snacks:					
Coffees/teas:	Fluid intake:	Totals:			

WEDNESDAY		kJ/Cal	Fat	Protein	Carbs
Breakfast Time: am/pm					
Lunch Time: am/pm					
Dinner Time: am/pm					
Snacks:					
Coffees/teas:	Fluid intake:	Totals:			

THURSDAY		kJ/Cal	Fat	Protein	Carbs
Breakfast Time: am/pm					
Lunch Time: am/pm					
Dinner Time: am/pm					
Snacks:					
Coffees/teas:	Fluid intake:	Totals:			

FRIDAY		kJ/Cal	Fat	Protein	Carbs
Breakfast Time: am/pm					
Lunch Time: am/pm					
Dinner Time: am/pm					
Snacks:					
Coffees/teas:	Fluid intake:	Totals:			

SATURDAY		kJ/Cal	Fat	Protein	Carbs
Breakfast Time: am/pm					
Lunch Time: am/pm					
Dinner Time: am/pm					
Snacks:					
Coffees/teas:	Fluid intake:	Totals:			

SUNDAY		kJ/Cal	Fat	Protein	Carbs
Breakfast Time: am/pm					
Lunch Time: am/pm					
Dinner Time: am/pm					
Snacks:					
Coffees/teas:	Fluid intake:	Totals:			

Units of alcohol this week: ☐   Total alcohol kJ/Cal: ☐

Vitamins and supplements

Weekly Totals	kJ/Cal	Fat	Protein	Carbs

Weekly Personal Summary

Energy level [1–5] ☐   Stress level [1–5] ☐

Hours of sleep ☐   Sleep quality [1–5] ☐

Mood [1–5] ☐   Appetite [1–5] ☐

kJ/Cal intake

Planned kJ/Cal	
Actual kJ/Cal	

Difference [+/-] ☐

Weight at start of week ☐
Weight at end of week ☐
BMI at start of week ☐
BMI at end of week ☐

Injuries or illnesses ☐

Week Beginning

[/   /   ]

Planned exercise sessions this week

	Exercise	Completed [Y/N]
Monday		
Tuesday		
Wednesday		
Thursday		
Friday		
Saturday		
Sunday		

Strength Training

MONDAY

Focus area	Equipment	SET 1		SET 2		SET 3		SET 4	
		Weight	Reps	Weight	Reps	Weight	Reps	Weight	Reps

TUESDAY

Focus area	Equipment	SET 1		SET 2		SET 3		SET 4	
		Weight	Reps	Weight	Reps	Weight	Reps	Weight	Reps

WEDNESDAY

Focus area	Equipment	SET 1		SET 2		SET 3		SET 4	
		Weight	Reps	Weight	Reps	Weight	Reps	Weight	Reps

THURSDAY

Focus area	Equipment	SET 1		SET 2		SET 3		SET 4	
		Weight	Reps	Weight	Reps	Weight	Reps	Weight	Reps

FRIDAY

Focus area	Equipment	SET 1		SET 2		SET 3		SET 4	
		Weight	Reps	Weight	Reps	Weight	Reps	Weight	Reps

SATURDAY

Focus area	Equipment	SET 1		SET 2		SET 3		SET 4	
		Weight	Reps	Weight	Reps	Weight	Reps	Weight	Reps

SUNDAY

Focus area	Equipment	SET 1		SET 2		SET 3		SET 4	
		Weight	Reps	Weight	Reps	Weight	Reps	Weight	Reps

Cardio Training

	Exercise	Time	Distance/resistance	Intensity	Heart rate	Ease	kJ/Cal expended
MONDAY							
							Total:

	Exercise	Time	Distance/resistance	Intensity	Heart rate	Ease	kJ/Cal expended
TUESDAY							
							Total:

	Exercise	Time	Distance/resistance	Intensity	Heart rate	Ease	kJ/Cal expended
WEDNESDAY							
							Total:

	Exercise	Time	Distance/resistance	Intensity	Heart rate	Ease	kJ/Cal expended
THURSDAY							
							Total:

	Exercise	Time	Distance/resistance	Intensity	Heart rate	Ease	kJ/Cal expended
FRIDAY							
							Total:

	Exercise	Time	Distance/resistance	Intensity	Heart rate	Ease	kJ/Cal expended
SATURDAY							
							Total:

	Exercise	Time	Distance/resistance	Intensity	Heart rate	Ease	kJ/Cal expended
SUNDAY							
							Total:

Weekly Total:

Food Diary

MONDAY		kJ/Cal	Fat	Protein	Carbs
Breakfast Time: am/pm					
Lunch Time: am/pm					
Dinner Time: am/pm					
Snacks:					
Coffees/teas:	Fluid intake:	Totals:			

TUESDAY		kJ/Cal	Fat	Protein	Carbs
Breakfast Time: am/pm					
Lunch Time: am/pm					
Dinner Time: am/pm					
Snacks:					
Coffees/teas:	Fluid intake:	Totals:			

WEDNESDAY		kJ/Cal	Fat	Protein	Carbs
Breakfast Time: am/pm					
Lunch Time: am/pm					
Dinner Time: am/pm					
Snacks:					
Coffees/teas:	Fluid intake:	Totals:			

THURSDAY		kJ/Cal	Fat	Protein	Carbs
Breakfast Time: am/pm					
Lunch Time: am/pm					
Dinner Time: am/pm					
Snacks:					
Coffees/teas:	Fluid intake:	Totals:			

FRIDAY			kJ/Cal	Fat	Protein	Carbs
Breakfast Time: am/pm						
Lunch Time: am/pm						
Dinner Time: am/pm						
Snacks:						
Coffees/teas:	Fluid intake:	Totals:				

SATURDAY			kJ/Cal	Fat	Protein	Carbs
Breakfast Time: am/pm						
Lunch Time: am/pm						
Dinner Time: am/pm						
Snacks:						
Coffees/teas:	Fluid intake:	Totals:				

SUNDAY			kJ/Cal	Fat	Protein	Carbs
Breakfast Time: am/pm						
Lunch Time: am/pm						
Dinner Time: am/pm						
Snacks:						
Coffees/teas:	Fluid intake:	Totals:				

Units of alcohol this week: _____   Total alcohol kJ/Cal: _____

Vitamins and supplements

Weekly Totals	kJ/Cal	Fat	Protein	Carbs

Weekly Personal Summary

Energy level 1–5 ___   Stress level 1–5 ___

Hours of sleep ___   Sleep quality 1–5 ___

Mood 1–5 ___   Appetite 1–5 ___

kJ/Cal intake

Planned kJ/Cal _____
Actual kJ/Cal _____
Difference [+/-] _____

Weight at start of week _____
Weight at end of week _____
BMI at start of week _____
BMI at end of week _____

Injuries or illnesses _____

Week Beginning

[/ /]

Planned exercise sessions this week

	Exercise	Completed [Y/N]
Monday		
Tuesday		
Wednesday		
Thursday		
Friday		
Saturday		
Sunday		

Strength Training

MONDAY

Focus area	Equipment	SET 1		SET 2		SET 3		SET 4	
		Weight	Reps	Weight	Reps	Weight	Reps	Weight	Reps

TUESDAY

Focus area	Equipment	SET 1		SET 2		SET 3		SET 4	
		Weight	Reps	Weight	Reps	Weight	Reps	Weight	Reps

WEDNESDAY

Focus area	Equipment	SET 1		SET 2		SET 3		SET 4	
		Weight	Reps	Weight	Reps	Weight	Reps	Weight	Reps

THURSDAY

Focus area	Equipment	SET 1		SET 2		SET 3		SET 4	
		Weight	Reps	Weight	Reps	Weight	Reps	Weight	Reps

FRIDAY

Focus area	Equipment	SET 1		SET 2		SET 3		SET 4	
		Weight	Reps	Weight	Reps	Weight	Reps	Weight	Reps

SATURDAY

Focus area	Equipment	SET 1		SET 2		SET 3		SET 4	
		Weight	Reps	Weight	Reps	Weight	Reps	Weight	Reps

SUNDAY

Focus area	Equipment	SET 1		SET 2		SET 3		SET 4	
		Weight	Reps	Weight	Reps	Weight	Reps	Weight	Reps

Cardio Training

	Exercise	Time	Distance/resistance	Intensity	Heart rate	Ease	kJ/Cal expended
MONDAY							
							Total:

	Exercise	Time	Distance/resistance	Intensity	Heart rate	Ease	kJ/Cal expended
TUESDAY							
							Total:

	Exercise	Time	Distance/resistance	Intensity	Heart rate	Ease	kJ/Cal expended
WEDNESDAY							
							Total:

	Exercise	Time	Distance/resistance	Intensity	Heart rate	Ease	kJ/Cal expended
THURSDAY							
							Total:

	Exercise	Time	Distance/resistance	Intensity	Heart rate	Ease	kJ/Cal expended
FRIDAY							
							Total:

	Exercise	Time	Distance/resistance	Intensity	Heart rate	Ease	kJ/Cal expended
SATURDAY							
							Total:

	Exercise	Time	Distance/resistance	Intensity	Heart rate	Ease	kJ/Cal expended
SUNDAY							
							Total:

Weekly Total:

Food Diary

MONDAY		kJ/Cal	Fat	Protein	Carbs
Breakfast Time: am/pm					
Lunch Time: am/pm					
Dinner Time: am/pm					
Snacks:					
Coffees/teas:	Fluid intake:	Totals:			

TUESDAY		kJ/Cal	Fat	Protein	Carbs
Breakfast Time: am/pm					
Lunch Time: am/pm					
Dinner Time: am/pm					
Snacks:					
Coffees/teas:	Fluid intake:	Totals:			

WEDNESDAY		kJ/Cal	Fat	Protein	Carbs
Breakfast Time: am/pm					
Lunch Time: am/pm					
Dinner Time: am/pm					
Snacks:					
Coffees/teas:	Fluid intake:	Totals:			

THURSDAY		kJ/Cal	Fat	Protein	Carbs
Breakfast Time: am/pm					
Lunch Time: am/pm					
Dinner Time: am/pm					
Snacks:					
Coffees/teas:	Fluid intake:	Totals:			

FRIDAY		kJ/Cal	Fat	Protein	Carbs
Breakfast Time: am/pm					
Lunch Time: am/pm					
Dinner Time: am/pm					
Snacks:					
Coffees/teas:	Fluid intake:	Totals:			

SATURDAY		kJ/Cal	Fat	Protein	Carbs
Breakfast Time: am/pm					
Lunch Time: am/pm					
Dinner Time: am/pm					
Snacks:					
Coffees/teas:	Fluid intake:	Totals:			

SUNDAY		kJ/Cal	Fat	Protein	Carbs
Breakfast Time: am/pm					
Lunch Time: am/pm					
Dinner Time: am/pm					
Snacks:					
Coffees/teas:	Fluid intake:	Totals:			

Units of alcohol this week: [   ]   Total alcohol kJ/Cal: [   ]

Vitamins and supplements

	kJ/Cal	Fat	Protein	Carbs
Weekly Totals				

Weekly Personal Summary

Energy level 1–5 [ ]   Stress level 1–5 [ ]

Hours of sleep [ ]   Sleep quality 1–5 [ ]

Mood 1–5 [ ]   Appetite 1–5 [ ]

kJ/Cal intake

Planned kJ/Cal	
Actual kJ/Cal	
Difference [+/-]	

Weight at start of week [ ]

Weight at end of week [ ]

BMI at start of week [ ]

BMI at end of week [ ]

Injuries or illnesses [   ]

Week Beginning

[/ /]

Planned exercise sessions this week

	Exercise	Completed [Y/N]
Monday		
Tuesday		
Wednesday		
Thursday		
Friday		
Saturday		
Sunday		

Strength Training

MONDAY

Focus area	Equipment	SET 1		SET 2		SET 3		SET 4	
		Weight	Reps	Weight	Reps	Weight	Reps	Weight	Reps

TUESDAY

Focus area	Equipment	SET 1		SET 2		SET 3		SET 4	
		Weight	Reps	Weight	Reps	Weight	Reps	Weight	Reps

WEDNESDAY

Focus area	Equipment	SET 1		SET 2		SET 3		SET 4	
		Weight	Reps	Weight	Reps	Weight	Reps	Weight	Reps

THURSDAY

Focus area	Equipment	SET 1		SET 2		SET 3		SET 4	
		Weight	Reps	Weight	Reps	Weight	Reps	Weight	Reps

FRIDAY

Focus area	Equipment	SET 1		SET 2		SET 3		SET 4	
		Weight	Reps	Weight	Reps	Weight	Reps	Weight	Reps

SATURDAY

Focus area	Equipment	SET 1		SET 2		SET 3		SET 4	
		Weight	Reps	Weight	Reps	Weight	Reps	Weight	Reps

SUNDAY

Focus area	Equipment	SET 1		SET 2		SET 3		SET 4	
		Weight	Reps	Weight	Reps	Weight	Reps	Weight	Reps

Cardio Training

MONDAY	Exercise	Time	Distance/resistance	Intensity	Heart rate	Ease	kJ/Cal expended
							Total:

TUESDAY	Exercise	Time	Distance/resistance	Intensity	Heart rate	Ease	kJ/Cal expended
							Total:

WEDNESDAY	Exercise	Time	Distance/resistance	Intensity	Heart rate	Ease	kJ/Cal expended
							Total:

THURSDAY	Exercise	Time	Distance/resistance	Intensity	Heart rate	Ease	kJ/Cal expended
							Total:

FRIDAY	Exercise	Time	Distance/resistance	Intensity	Heart rate	Ease	kJ/Cal expended
							Total:

SATURDAY	Exercise	Time	Distance/resistance	Intensity	Heart rate	Ease	kJ/Cal expended
							Total:

SUNDAY	Exercise	Time	Distance/resistance	Intensity	Heart rate	Ease	kJ/Cal expended
							Total:

Weekly Total:

Food Diary

MONDAY		kJ/Cal	Fat	Protein	Carbs
Breakfast Time: am/pm					
Lunch Time: am/pm					
Dinner Time: am/pm					
Snacks:					
Coffees/teas:	**Fluid intake:**	**Totals:**			

TUESDAY		kJ/Cal	Fat	Protein	Carbs
Breakfast Time: am/pm					
Lunch Time: am/pm					
Dinner Time: am/pm					
Snacks:					
Coffees/teas:	**Fluid intake:**	**Totals:**			

WEDNESDAY		kJ/Cal	Fat	Protein	Carbs
Breakfast Time: am/pm					
Lunch Time: am/pm					
Dinner Time: am/pm					
Snacks:					
Coffees/teas:	**Fluid intake:**	**Totals:**			

THURSDAY		kJ/Cal	Fat	Protein	Carbs
Breakfast Time: am/pm					
Lunch Time: am/pm					
Dinner Time: am/pm					
Snacks:					
Coffees/teas:	**Fluid intake:**	**Totals:**			

FRIDAY		kJ/Cal	Fat	Protein	Carbs
Breakfast Time: am/pm					
Lunch Time: am/pm					
Dinner Time: am/pm					
Snacks:					
Coffees/teas:	Fluid intake:	Totals:			

SATURDAY		kJ/Cal	Fat	Protein	Carbs
Breakfast Time: am/pm					
Lunch Time: am/pm					
Dinner Time: am/pm					
Snacks:					
Coffees/teas:	Fluid intake:	Totals:			

SUNDAY		kJ/Cal	Fat	Protein	Carbs
Breakfast Time: am/pm					
Lunch Time: am/pm					
Dinner Time: am/pm					
Snacks:					
Coffees/teas:	Fluid intake:	Totals:			

Units of alcohol this week: ☐   Total alcohol kJ/Cal: ☐

Vitamins and supplements

Weekly Totals	kJ/Cal	Fat	Protein	Carbs

Weekly Personal Summary

Energy level [1–5] ☐   Stress level [1–5] ☐

Hours of sleep ☐   Sleep quality [1–5] ☐

Mood [1–5] ☐   Appetite [1–5] ☐

kJ/Cal intake

| Planned kJ/Cal | |
| Actual kJ/Cal | |

Difference [+/-] ☐

Weight at start of week ☐

Weight at end of week ☐

BMI at start of week ☐

BMI at end of week ☐

Injuries or illnesses ☐

Week Beginning

[ ] / [ ] / [ ]

Planned exercise sessions this week

	Exercise	Completed [Y/N]
Monday		
Tuesday		
Wednesday		
Thursday		
Friday		
Saturday		
Sunday		

Strength Training

MONDAY

Focus area	Equipment	SET 1		SET 2		SET 3		SET 4	
		Weight	Reps	Weight	Reps	Weight	Reps	Weight	Reps

TUESDAY

Focus area	Equipment	SET 1		SET 2		SET 3		SET 4	
		Weight	Reps	Weight	Reps	Weight	Reps	Weight	Reps

WEDNESDAY

Focus area	Equipment	SET 1		SET 2		SET 3		SET 4	
		Weight	Reps	Weight	Reps	Weight	Reps	Weight	Reps

THURSDAY

Focus area	Equipment	SET 1		SET 2		SET 3		SET 4	
		Weight	Reps	Weight	Reps	Weight	Reps	Weight	Reps

FRIDAY

Focus area	Equipment	SET 1		SET 2		SET 3		SET 4	
		Weight	Reps	Weight	Reps	Weight	Reps	Weight	Reps

SATURDAY

Focus area	Equipment	SET 1		SET 2		SET 3		SET 4	
		Weight	Reps	Weight	Reps	Weight	Reps	Weight	Reps

SUNDAY

Focus area	Equipment	SET 1		SET 2		SET 3		SET 4	
		Weight	Reps	Weight	Reps	Weight	Reps	Weight	Reps

Cardio Training

	Exercise	Time	Distance/resistance	Intensity	Heart rate	Ease	kJ/Cal expended
MONDAY							
							Total:

	Exercise	Time	Distance/resistance	Intensity	Heart rate	Ease	kJ/Cal expended
TUESDAY							
							Total:

	Exercise	Time	Distance/resistance	Intensity	Heart rate	Ease	kJ/Cal expended
WEDNESDAY							
							Total:

	Exercise	Time	Distance/resistance	Intensity	Heart rate	Ease	kJ/Cal expended
THURSDAY							
							Total:

	Exercise	Time	Distance/resistance	Intensity	Heart rate	Ease	kJ/Cal expended
FRIDAY							
							Total:

	Exercise	Time	Distance/resistance	Intensity	Heart rate	Ease	kJ/Cal expended
SATURDAY							
							Total:

	Exercise	Time	Distance/resistance	Intensity	Heart rate	Ease	kJ/Cal expended
SUNDAY							
							Total:

Weekly Total:

Food Diary

MONDAY		kJ/Cal	Fat	Protein	Carbs
Breakfast Time: am/pm					
Lunch Time: am/pm					
Dinner Time: am/pm					
Snacks:					
Coffees/teas:	Fluid intake: Totals:				

TUESDAY		kJ/Cal	Fat	Protein	Carbs
Breakfast Time: am/pm					
Lunch Time: am/pm					
Dinner Time: am/pm					
Snacks:					
Coffees/teas:	Fluid intake: Totals:				

WEDNESDAY		kJ/Cal	Fat	Protein	Carbs
Breakfast Time: am/pm					
Lunch Time: am/pm					
Dinner Time: am/pm					
Snacks:					
Coffees/teas:	Fluid intake: Totals:				

THURSDAY		kJ/Cal	Fat	Protein	Carbs
Breakfast Time: am/pm					
Lunch Time: am/pm					
Dinner Time: am/pm					
Snacks:					
Coffees/teas:	Fluid intake: Totals:				

FRIDAY			kJ/Cal	Fat	Protein	Carbs
Breakfast Time: am/pm						
Lunch Time: am/pm						
Dinner Time: am/pm						
Snacks:						
Coffees/teas:	Fluid intake:	Totals:				

SATURDAY			kJ/Cal	Fat	Protein	Carbs
Breakfast Time: am/pm						
Lunch Time: am/pm						
Dinner Time: am/pm						
Snacks:						
Coffees/teas:	Fluid intake:	Totals:				

SUNDAY			kJ/Cal	Fat	Protein	Carbs
Breakfast Time: am/pm						
Lunch Time: am/pm						
Dinner Time: am/pm						
Snacks:						
Coffees/teas:	Fluid intake:	Totals:				

Units of alcohol this week: [ ]   Total alcohol kJ/Cal: [ ]

Vitamins and supplements

Weekly Totals	kJ/Cal	Fat	Protein	Carbs

Weekly Personal Summary

Energy level [ ] 1–5   Stress level [ ] 1–5

Hours of sleep [ ]   Sleep quality [ ] 1–5

Mood [ ] 1–5   Appetite [ ] 1–5

kJ/Cal intake

| Planned kJ/Cal | |
| Actual kJ/Cal | |

Difference [+/-] [ ]

Weight at start of week [ ]

Weight at end of week [ ]

BMI at start of week [ ]

BMI at end of week [ ]

Injuries or illnesses [ ]

Week Beginning

[ ] / [ ] / [ ]

Planned exercise sessions this week

	Exercise	Completed [Y/N]
Monday		
Tuesday		
Wednesday		
Thursday		
Friday		
Saturday		
Sunday		

Strength Training

MONDAY

Focus area	Equipment	SET 1		SET 2		SET 3		SET 4	
		Weight	Reps	Weight	Reps	Weight	Reps	Weight	Reps

TUESDAY

Focus area	Equipment	SET 1		SET 2		SET 3		SET 4	
		Weight	Reps	Weight	Reps	Weight	Reps	Weight	Reps

WEDNESDAY

Focus area	Equipment	SET 1		SET 2		SET 3		SET 4	
		Weight	Reps	Weight	Reps	Weight	Reps	Weight	Reps

THURSDAY

Focus area	Equipment	SET 1		SET 2		SET 3		SET 4	
		Weight	Reps	Weight	Reps	Weight	Reps	Weight	Reps

FRIDAY

Focus area	Equipment	SET 1		SET 2		SET 3		SET 4	
		Weight	Reps	Weight	Reps	Weight	Reps	Weight	Reps

SATURDAY

Focus area	Equipment	SET 1		SET 2		SET 3		SET 4	
		Weight	Reps	Weight	Reps	Weight	Reps	Weight	Reps

SUNDAY

Focus area	Equipment	SET 1		SET 2		SET 3		SET 4	
		Weight	Reps	Weight	Reps	Weight	Reps	Weight	Reps

Cardio Training

MONDAY	Exercise	Time	Distance/resistance	Intensity	Heart rate	Ease	kJ/Cal expended
							Total:

TUESDAY	Exercise	Time	Distance/resistance	Intensity	Heart rate	Ease	kJ/Cal expended
							Total:

WEDNESDAY	Exercise	Time	Distance/resistance	Intensity	Heart rate	Ease	kJ/Cal expended
							Total:

THURSDAY	Exercise	Time	Distance/resistance	Intensity	Heart rate	Ease	kJ/Cal expended
							Total:

FRIDAY	Exercise	Time	Distance/resistance	Intensity	Heart rate	Ease	kJ/Cal expended
							Total:

SATURDAY	Exercise	Time	Distance/resistance	Intensity	Heart rate	Ease	kJ/Cal expended
							Total:

SUNDAY	Exercise	Time	Distance/resistance	Intensity	Heart rate	Ease	kJ/Cal expended
							Total:

Weekly Total:

Food Diary

MONDAY		kJ/Cal	Fat	Protein	Carbs
Breakfast Time: am/pm					
Lunch Time: am/pm					
Dinner Time: am/pm					
Snacks:					
Coffees/teas:	**Fluid intake:** **Totals:**				

TUESDAY		kJ/Cal	Fat	Protein	Carbs
Breakfast Time: am/pm					
Lunch Time: am/pm					
Dinner Time: am/pm					
Snacks:					
Coffees/teas:	**Fluid intake:** **Totals:**				

WEDNESDAY		kJ/Cal	Fat	Protein	Carbs
Breakfast Time: am/pm					
Lunch Time: am/pm					
Dinner Time: am/pm					
Snacks:					
Coffees/teas:	**Fluid intake:** **Totals:**				

THURSDAY		kJ/Cal	Fat	Protein	Carbs
Breakfast Time: am/pm					
Lunch Time: am/pm					
Dinner Time: am/pm					
Snacks:					
Coffees/teas:	**Fluid intake:** **Totals:**				

FRIDAY		kJ/Cal	Fat	Protein	Carbs
Breakfast Time: am/pm					
Lunch Time: am/pm					
Dinner Time: am/pm					
Snacks:					
Coffees/teas:	Fluid intake:	Totals:			

SATURDAY		kJ/Cal	Fat	Protein	Carbs
Breakfast Time: am/pm					
Lunch Time: am/pm					
Dinner Time: am/pm					
Snacks:					
Coffees/teas:	Fluid intake:	Totals:			

SUNDAY		kJ/Cal	Fat	Protein	Carbs
Breakfast Time: am/pm					
Lunch Time: am/pm					
Dinner Time: am/pm					
Snacks:					
Coffees/teas:	Fluid intake:	Totals:			

Units of alcohol this week: Total alcohol kJ/Cal:

Vitamins and supplements

Weekly Totals	kJ/Cal	Fat	Protein	Carbs

Weekly Personal Summary

Energy level 1–5   Stress level 1–5

Hours of sleep   Sleep quality 1–5

Mood 1–5   Appetite 1–5

kJ/Cal intake
- Planned kJ/Cal
- Actual kJ/Cal
- Difference [+/-]

Weight at start of week
Weight at end of week
BMI at start of week
BMI at end of week

Injuries or illnesses

149

Week Beginning

[   ] / [   ] / [   ]

	Exercise	Completed [Y/N]
Monday		
Tuesday		
Wednesday		
Thursday		
Friday		
Saturday		
Sunday		

Strength Training

MONDAY

Focus area	Equipment	SET 1		SET 2		SET 3		SET 4	
		Weight	Reps	Weight	Reps	Weight	Reps	Weight	Reps

TUESDAY

Focus area	Equipment	SET 1		SET 2		SET 3		SET 4	
		Weight	Reps	Weight	Reps	Weight	Reps	Weight	Reps

WEDNESDAY

Focus area	Equipment	SET 1		SET 2		SET 3		SET 4	
		Weight	Reps	Weight	Reps	Weight	Reps	Weight	Reps

THURSDAY

Focus area	Equipment	SET 1		SET 2		SET 3		SET 4	
		Weight	Reps	Weight	Reps	Weight	Reps	Weight	Reps

FRIDAY

Focus area	Equipment	SET 1		SET 2		SET 3		SET 4	
		Weight	Reps	Weight	Reps	Weight	Reps	Weight	Reps

SATURDAY

Focus area	Equipment	SET 1		SET 2		SET 3		SET 4	
		Weight	Reps	Weight	Reps	Weight	Reps	Weight	Reps

SUNDAY

Focus area	Equipment	SET 1		SET 2		SET 3		SET 4	
		Weight	Reps	Weight	Reps	Weight	Reps	Weight	Reps

Cardio Training

MONDAY	Exercise	Time	Distance/resistance	Intensity	Heart rate	Ease	kJ/Cal expended
							Total:

TUESDAY	Exercise	Time	Distance/resistance	Intensity	Heart rate	Ease	kJ/Cal expended
							Total:

WEDNESDAY	Exercise	Time	Distance/resistance	Intensity	Heart rate	Ease	kJ/Cal expended
							Total:

THURSDAY	Exercise	Time	Distance/resistance	Intensity	Heart rate	Ease	kJ/Cal expended
							Total:

FRIDAY	Exercise	Time	Distance/resistance	Intensity	Heart rate	Ease	kJ/Cal expended
							Total:

SATURDAY	Exercise	Time	Distance/resistance	Intensity	Heart rate	Ease	kJ/Cal expended
							Total:

SUNDAY	Exercise	Time	Distance/resistance	Intensity	Heart rate	Ease	kJ/Cal expended
							Total:

Weekly Total:

Food Diary

MONDAY		kJ/Cal	Fat	Protein	Carbs
Breakfast Time: am/pm					
Lunch Time: am/pm					
Dinner Time: am/pm					
Snacks:					
Coffees/teas:	**Fluid intake:** **Totals:**				

TUESDAY		kJ/Cal	Fat	Protein	Carbs
Breakfast Time: am/pm					
Lunch Time: am/pm					
Dinner Time: am/pm					
Snacks:					
Coffees/teas:	**Fluid intake:** **Totals:**				

WEDNESDAY		kJ/Cal	Fat	Protein	Carbs
Breakfast Time: am/pm					
Lunch Time: am/pm					
Dinner Time: am/pm					
Snacks:					
Coffees/teas:	**Fluid intake:** **Totals:**				

THURSDAY		kJ/Cal	Fat	Protein	Carbs
Breakfast Time: am/pm					
Lunch Time: am/pm					
Dinner Time: am/pm					
Snacks:					
Coffees/teas:	**Fluid intake:** **Totals:**				

FRIDAY			kJ/Cal	Fat	Protein	Carbs
Breakfast Time: am/pm						
Lunch Time: am/pm						
Dinner Time: am/pm						
Snacks:						
Coffees/teas:	Fluid intake:	Totals:				

SATURDAY			kJ/Cal	Fat	Protein	Carbs
Breakfast Time: am/pm						
Lunch Time: am/pm						
Dinner Time: am/pm						
Snacks:						
Coffees/teas:	Fluid intake:	Totals:				

SUNDAY			kJ/Cal	Fat	Protein	Carbs
Breakfast Time: am/pm						
Lunch Time: am/pm						
Dinner Time: am/pm						
Snacks:						
Coffees/teas:	Fluid intake:	Totals:				

Units of alcohol this week: [ ]   Total alcohol kJ/Cal: [ ]

Vitamins and supplements

Weekly Totals	kJ/Cal	Fat	Protein	Carbs

Weekly Personal Summary

Energy level [ ] 1–5   Stress level [ ] 1–5

Hours of sleep [ ]   Sleep quality [ ] 1–5

Mood [ ] 1–5   Appetite [ ] 1–5

kJ/Cal intake

Planned kJ/Cal	
Actual kJ/Cal	

Difference [+/-] [ ]

Weight at start of week [ ]

Weight at end of week [ ]

BMI at start of week [ ]

BMI at end of week [ ]

Injuries or illnesses [ ]

Week Beginning

/ /

	Exercise	Completed [Y/N]
Monday		
Tuesday		
Wednesday		
Thursday		
Friday		
Saturday		
Sunday		

Strength Training

MONDAY

Focus area	Equipment	SET 1		SET 2		SET 3		SET 4	
		Weight	Reps	Weight	Reps	Weight	Reps	Weight	Reps

TUESDAY

Focus area	Equipment	SET 1		SET 2		SET 3		SET 4	
		Weight	Reps	Weight	Reps	Weight	Reps	Weight	Reps

WEDNESDAY

Focus area	Equipment	SET 1		SET 2		SET 3		SET 4	
		Weight	Reps	Weight	Reps	Weight	Reps	Weight	Reps

THURSDAY

Focus area	Equipment	SET 1		SET 2		SET 3		SET 4	
		Weight	Reps	Weight	Reps	Weight	Reps	Weight	Reps

FRIDAY

Focus area	Equipment	SET 1		SET 2		SET 3		SET 4	
		Weight	Reps	Weight	Reps	Weight	Reps	Weight	Reps

SATURDAY

Focus area	Equipment	SET 1		SET 2		SET 3		SET 4	
		Weight	Reps	Weight	Reps	Weight	Reps	Weight	Reps

SUNDAY

Focus area	Equipment	SET 1		SET 2		SET 3		SET 4	
		Weight	Reps	Weight	Reps	Weight	Reps	Weight	Reps

Cardio Training

MONDAY

Exercise	Time	Distance/resistance	Intensity	Heart rate	Ease	kJ/Cal expended
						Total:

TUESDAY

Exercise	Time	Distance/resistance	Intensity	Heart rate	Ease	kJ/Cal expended
						Total:

WEDNESDAY

Exercise	Time	Distance/resistance	Intensity	Heart rate	Ease	kJ/Cal expended
						Total:

THURSDAY

Exercise	Time	Distance/resistance	Intensity	Heart rate	Ease	kJ/Cal expended
						Total:

FRIDAY

Exercise	Time	Distance/resistance	Intensity	Heart rate	Ease	kJ/Cal expended
						Total:

SATURDAY

Exercise	Time	Distance/resistance	Intensity	Heart rate	Ease	kJ/Cal expended
						Total:

SUNDAY

Exercise	Time	Distance/resistance	Intensity	Heart rate	Ease	kJ/Cal expended
						Total:

Weekly Total:

Food Diary

MONDAY		kJ/Cal	Fat	Protein	Carbs
Breakfast Time: am/pm					
Lunch Time: am/pm					
Dinner Time: am/pm					
Snacks:					
Coffees/teas:	Fluid intake:	Totals:			

TUESDAY		kJ/Cal	Fat	Protein	Carbs
Breakfast Time: am/pm					
Lunch Time: am/pm					
Dinner Time: am/pm					
Snacks:					
Coffees/teas:	Fluid intake:	Totals:			

WEDNESDAY		kJ/Cal	Fat	Protein	Carbs
Breakfast Time: am/pm					
Lunch Time: am/pm					
Dinner Time: am/pm					
Snacks:					
Coffees/teas:	Fluid intake:	Totals:			

THURSDAY		kJ/Cal	Fat	Protein	Carbs
Breakfast Time: am/pm					
Lunch Time: am/pm					
Dinner Time: am/pm					
Snacks:					
Coffees/teas:	Fluid intake:	Totals:			

FRIDAY		kJ/Cal	Fat	Protein	Carbs
Breakfast Time: am/pm					
Lunch Time: am/pm					
Dinner Time: am/pm					
Snacks:					
Coffees/teas:	**Fluid intake:**	**Totals:**			

SATURDAY		kJ/Cal	Fat	Protein	Carbs
Breakfast Time: am/pm					
Lunch Time: am/pm					
Dinner Time: am/pm					
Snacks:					
Coffees/teas:	**Fluid intake:**	**Totals:**			

SUNDAY		kJ/Cal	Fat	Protein	Carbs
Breakfast Time: am/pm					
Lunch Time: am/pm					
Dinner Time: am/pm					
Snacks:					
Coffees/teas:	**Fluid intake:**	**Totals:**			

Units of alcohol this week: [   ]   **Total alcohol kJ/Cal:** [   ]

Vitamins and supplements

Weekly Totals	kJ/Cal	Fat	Protein	Carbs

Weekly Personal Summary

Energy level [ ] 1–5   Stress level [ ] 1–5

Hours of sleep [ ]   Sleep quality [ ] 1–5

Mood [ ] 1–5   Appetite [ ] 1–5

kJ/Cal intake

Planned kJ/Cal	
Actual kJ/Cal	
Difference [+/-]	

Weight at start of week [ ]

Weight at end of week [ ]

BMI at start of week [ ]

BMI at end of week [ ]

Injuries or illnesses [   ]

Week Beginning

[ ] / [ ] / [ ]

Planned exercise sessions this week

	Exercise	Completed [Y/N]
Monday		
Tuesday		
Wednesday		
Thursday		
Friday		
Saturday		
Sunday		

Strength Training

MONDAY

Focus area	Equipment	SET 1		SET 2		SET 3		SET 4	
		Weight	Reps	Weight	Reps	Weight	Reps	Weight	Reps

TUESDAY

Focus area	Equipment	SET 1		SET 2		SET 3		SET 4	
		Weight	Reps	Weight	Reps	Weight	Reps	Weight	Reps

WEDNESDAY

Focus area	Equipment	SET 1		SET 2		SET 3		SET 4	
		Weight	Reps	Weight	Reps	Weight	Reps	Weight	Reps

THURSDAY

Focus area	Equipment	SET 1		SET 2		SET 3		SET 4	
		Weight	Reps	Weight	Reps	Weight	Reps	Weight	Reps

FRIDAY

Focus area	Equipment	SET 1		SET 2		SET 3		SET 4	
		Weight	Reps	Weight	Reps	Weight	Reps	Weight	Reps

SATURDAY

Focus area	Equipment	SET 1		SET 2		SET 3		SET 4	
		Weight	Reps	Weight	Reps	Weight	Reps	Weight	Reps

SUNDAY

Focus area	Equipment	SET 1		SET 2		SET 3		SET 4	
		Weight	Reps	Weight	Reps	Weight	Reps	Weight	Reps

Cardio Training

	Exercise	Time	Distance/ resistance	Intensity	Heart rate	Ease	kJ/Cal expended
MONDAY							
							Total:

	Exercise	Time	Distance/ resistance	Intensity	Heart rate	Ease	kJ/Cal expended
TUESDAY							
							Total:

	Exercise	Time	Distance/ resistance	Intensity	Heart rate	Ease	kJ/Cal expended
WEDNESDAY							
							Total:

	Exercise	Time	Distance/ resistance	Intensity	Heart rate	Ease	kJ/Cal expended
THURSDAY							
							Total:

	Exercise	Time	Distance/ resistance	Intensity	Heart rate	Ease	kJ/Cal expended
FRIDAY							
							Total:

	Exercise	Time	Distance/ resistance	Intensity	Heart rate	Ease	kJ/Cal expended
SATURDAY							
							Total:

	Exercise	Time	Distance/ resistance	Intensity	Heart rate	Ease	kJ/Cal expended
SUNDAY							
							Total:

Weekly Total:

Food Diary

MONDAY		kJ/Cal	Fat	Protein	Carbs
Breakfast Time: am/pm					
Lunch Time: am/pm					
Dinner Time: am/pm					
Snacks:					
Coffees/teas:	Fluid intake:	Totals:			

TUESDAY		kJ/Cal	Fat	Protein	Carbs
Breakfast Time: am/pm					
Lunch Time: am/pm					
Dinner Time: am/pm					
Snacks:					
Coffees/teas:	Fluid intake:	Totals:			

WEDNESDAY		kJ/Cal	Fat	Protein	Carbs
Breakfast Time: am/pm					
Lunch Time: am/pm					
Dinner Time: am/pm					
Snacks:					
Coffees/teas:	Fluid intake:	Totals:			

THURSDAY		kJ/Cal	Fat	Protein	Carbs
Breakfast Time: am/pm					
Lunch Time: am/pm					
Dinner Time: am/pm					
Snacks:					
Coffees/teas:	Fluid intake:	Totals:			

FRIDAY		kJ/Cal	Fat	Protein	Carbs
Breakfast Time: am/pm					
Lunch Time: am/pm					
Dinner Time: am/pm					
Snacks:					
Coffees/teas:	**Fluid intake:**	**Totals:**			

SATURDAY		kJ/Cal	Fat	Protein	Carbs
Breakfast Time: am/pm					
Lunch Time: am/pm					
Dinner Time: am/pm					
Snacks:					
Coffees/teas:	**Fluid intake:**	**Totals:**			

SUNDAY		kJ/Cal	Fat	Protein	Carbs
Breakfast Time: am/pm					
Lunch Time: am/pm					
Dinner Time: am/pm					
Snacks:					
Coffees/teas:	**Fluid intake:**	**Totals:**			

Units of alcohol this week: Total alcohol kJ/Cal:

Vitamins and supplements

Weekly Totals	kJ/Cal	Fat	Protein	Carbs

Weekly Personal Summary

Energy level 1–5   Stress level 1–5

Hours of sleep   Sleep quality 1–5

Mood 1–5   Appetite 1–5

kJ/Cal intake

Planned kJ/Cal	
Actual kJ/Cal	
Difference [+/-]	

Weight at start of week

Weight at end of week

BMI at start of week

BMI at end of week

Injuries or illnesses

161

Week Beginning

[ ] / [ ] /

Planned exercise sessions this week

	Exercise	Completed [Y/N]
Monday		
Tuesday		
Wednesday		
Thursday		
Friday		
Saturday		
Sunday		

Strength Training

MONDAY

Focus area	Equipment	SET 1		SET 2		SET 3		SET 4	
		Weight	Reps	Weight	Reps	Weight	Reps	Weight	Reps

TUESDAY

Focus area	Equipment	SET 1		SET 2		SET 3		SET 4	
		Weight	Reps	Weight	Reps	Weight	Reps	Weight	Reps

WEDNESDAY

Focus area	Equipment	SET 1		SET 2		SET 3		SET 4	
		Weight	Reps	Weight	Reps	Weight	Reps	Weight	Reps

THURSDAY

Focus area	Equipment	SET 1		SET 2		SET 3		SET 4	
		Weight	Reps	Weight	Reps	Weight	Reps	Weight	Reps

FRIDAY

Focus area	Equipment	SET 1		SET 2		SET 3		SET 4	
		Weight	Reps	Weight	Reps	Weight	Reps	Weight	Reps

SATURDAY

Focus area	Equipment	SET 1		SET 2		SET 3		SET 4	
		Weight	Reps	Weight	Reps	Weight	Reps	Weight	Reps

SUNDAY

Focus area	Equipment	SET 1		SET 2		SET 3		SET 4	
		Weight	Reps	Weight	Reps	Weight	Reps	Weight	Reps

Cardio Training

	Exercise	Time	Distance/resistance	Intensity	Heart rate	Ease	kJ/Cal expended
MONDAY							
							Total:

	Exercise	Time	Distance/resistance	Intensity	Heart rate	Ease	kJ/Cal expended
TUESDAY							
							Total:

	Exercise	Time	Distance/resistance	Intensity	Heart rate	Ease	kJ/Cal expended
WEDNESDAY							
							Total:

	Exercise	Time	Distance/resistance	Intensity	Heart rate	Ease	kJ/Cal expended
THURSDAY							
							Total:

	Exercise	Time	Distance/resistance	Intensity	Heart rate	Ease	kJ/Cal expended
FRIDAY							
							Total:

	Exercise	Time	Distance/resistance	Intensity	Heart rate	Ease	kJ/Cal expended
SATURDAY							
							Total:

	Exercise	Time	Distance/resistance	Intensity	Heart rate	Ease	kJ/Cal expended
SUNDAY							
							Total:
							Weekly Total:

Food Diary

MONDAY		kJ/Cal	Fat	Protein	Carbs
Breakfast Time: am/pm					
Lunch Time: am/pm					
Dinner Time: am/pm					
Snacks:					
Coffees/teas:	Fluid intake: Totals:				

TUESDAY		kJ/Cal	Fat	Protein	Carbs
Breakfast Time: am/pm					
Lunch Time: am/pm					
Dinner Time: am/pm					
Snacks:					
Coffees/teas:	Fluid intake: Totals:				

WEDNESDAY		kJ/Cal	Fat	Protein	Carbs
Breakfast Time: am/pm					
Lunch Time: am/pm					
Dinner Time: am/pm					
Snacks:					
Coffees/teas:	Fluid intake: Totals:				

THURSDAY		kJ/Cal	Fat	Protein	Carbs
Breakfast Time: am/pm					
Lunch Time: am/pm					
Dinner Time: am/pm					
Snacks:					
Coffees/teas:	Fluid intake: Totals:				

FRIDAY		kJ/Cal	Fat	Protein	Carbs
Breakfast Time: am/pm					
Lunch Time: am/pm					
Dinner Time: am/pm					
Snacks:					
Coffees/teas:	Fluid intake:	Totals:			

SATURDAY		kJ/Cal	Fat	Protein	Carbs
Breakfast Time: am/pm					
Lunch Time: am/pm					
Dinner Time: am/pm					
Snacks:					
Coffees/teas:	Fluid intake:	Totals:			

SUNDAY		kJ/Cal	Fat	Protein	Carbs
Breakfast Time: am/pm					
Lunch Time: am/pm					
Dinner Time: am/pm					
Snacks:					
Coffees/teas:	Fluid intake:	Totals:			

Units of alcohol this week: [ ]   Total alcohol kJ/Cal: [ ]

Vitamins and supplements

Weekly Totals	kJ/Cal	Fat	Protein	Carbs

Weekly Personal Summary

Energy level [ ] 1–5   Stress level [ ] 1–5

Hours of sleep [ ]   Sleep quality [ ] 1–5

Mood [ ] 1–5   Appetite [ ] 1–5

kJ/Cal intake

Planned kJ/Cal	
Actual kJ/Cal	

Difference [+/-] [ ]

Weight at start of week [ ]

Weight at end of week [ ]

BMI at start of week [ ]

BMI at end of week [ ]

Injuries or illnesses [ ]

Week Beginning

[/   /   ]

	Exercise	Completed [Y/N]
Monday		
Tuesday		
Wednesday		
Thursday		
Friday		
Saturday		
Sunday		

Strength Training

MONDAY

Focus area	Equipment	SET 1		SET 2		SET 3		SET 4	
		Weight	Reps	Weight	Reps	Weight	Reps	Weight	Reps

TUESDAY

Focus area	Equipment	SET 1		SET 2		SET 3		SET 4	
		Weight	Reps	Weight	Reps	Weight	Reps	Weight	Reps

WEDNESDAY

Focus area	Equipment	SET 1		SET 2		SET 3		SET 4	
		Weight	Reps	Weight	Reps	Weight	Reps	Weight	Reps

THURSDAY

Focus area	Equipment	SET 1		SET 2		SET 3		SET 4	
		Weight	Reps	Weight	Reps	Weight	Reps	Weight	Reps

FRIDAY

Focus area	Equipment	SET 1		SET 2		SET 3		SET 4	
		Weight	Reps	Weight	Reps	Weight	Reps	Weight	Reps

SATURDAY

Focus area	Equipment	SET 1		SET 2		SET 3		SET 4	
		Weight	Reps	Weight	Reps	Weight	Reps	Weight	Reps

SUNDAY

Focus area	Equipment	SET 1		SET 2		SET 3		SET 4	
		Weight	Reps	Weight	Reps	Weight	Reps	Weight	Reps

Cardio Training

MONDAY	Exercise	Time	Distance/ resistance	Intensity	Heart rate	Ease	kJ/Cal expended
							Total:

TUESDAY	Exercise	Time	Distance/ resistance	Intensity	Heart rate	Ease	kJ/Cal expended
							Total:

WEDNESDAY	Exercise	Time	Distance/ resistance	Intensity	Heart rate	Ease	kJ/Cal expended
							Total:

THURSDAY	Exercise	Time	Distance/ resistance	Intensity	Heart rate	Ease	kJ/Cal expended
							Total:

FRIDAY	Exercise	Time	Distance/ resistance	Intensity	Heart rate	Ease	kJ/Cal expended
							Total:

SATURDAY	Exercise	Time	Distance/ resistance	Intensity	Heart rate	Ease	kJ/Cal expended
							Total:

SUNDAY	Exercise	Time	Distance/ resistance	Intensity	Heart rate	Ease	kJ/Cal expended
							Total:

Weekly Total:

Food Diary

MONDAY		kJ/Cal	Fat	Protein	Carbs
Breakfast Time: am/pm					
Lunch Time: am/pm					
Dinner Time: am/pm					
Snacks:					
Coffees/teas:	Fluid intake:	Totals:			

TUESDAY		kJ/Cal	Fat	Protein	Carbs
Breakfast Time: am/pm					
Lunch Time: am/pm					
Dinner Time: am/pm					
Snacks:					
Coffees/teas:	Fluid intake:	Totals:			

WEDNESDAY		kJ/Cal	Fat	Protein	Carbs
Breakfast Time: am/pm					
Lunch Time: am/pm					
Dinner Time: am/pm					
Snacks:					
Coffees/teas:	Fluid intake:	Totals:			

THURSDAY		kJ/Cal	Fat	Protein	Carbs
Breakfast Time: am/pm					
Lunch Time: am/pm					
Dinner Time: am/pm					
Snacks:					
Coffees/teas:	Fluid intake:	Totals:			

FRIDAY			kJ/Cal	Fat	Protein	Carbs
Breakfast Time: am/pm						
Lunch Time: am/pm						
Dinner Time: am/pm						
Snacks:						
Coffees/teas:	**Fluid intake:**	**Totals:**				

SATURDAY			kJ/Cal	Fat	Protein	Carbs
Breakfast Time: am/pm						
Lunch Time: am/pm						
Dinner Time: am/pm						
Snacks:						
Coffees/teas:	**Fluid intake:**	**Totals:**				

SUNDAY			kJ/Cal	Fat	Protein	Carbs
Breakfast Time: am/pm						
Lunch Time: am/pm						
Dinner Time: am/pm						
Snacks:						
Coffees/teas:	**Fluid intake:**	**Totals:**				

Units of alcohol this week: [ ]   **Total alcohol kJ/Cal:** [ ]

Vitamins and supplements

Weekly Totals	kJ/Cal	Fat	Protein	Carbs

Weekly Personal Summary

Energy level [1–5] [ ]   **Stress level** [1–5] [ ]

Hours of sleep [ ]   **Sleep quality** [1–5] [ ]

Mood [1–5] [ ]   **Appetite** [1–5] [ ]

kJ/Cal intake

Planned kJ/Cal	
Actual kJ/Cal	

Difference [+/-] [ ]

Weight at start of week [ ]

Weight at end of week [ ]

BMI at start of week [ ]

BMI at end of week [ ]

Injuries or illnesses [ ]

Week Beginning

[/   /   ]

Planned exercise sessions this week

	Exercise	Completed [Y/N]
Monday		
Tuesday		
Wednesday		
Thursday		
Friday		
Saturday		
Sunday		

Strength Training

MONDAY

Focus area	Equipment	SET 1		SET 2		SET 3		SET 4	
		Weight	Reps	Weight	Reps	Weight	Reps	Weight	Reps

TUESDAY

Focus area	Equipment	SET 1		SET 2		SET 3		SET 4	
		Weight	Reps	Weight	Reps	Weight	Reps	Weight	Reps

WEDNESDAY

Focus area	Equipment	SET 1		SET 2		SET 3		SET 4	
		Weight	Reps	Weight	Reps	Weight	Reps	Weight	Reps

THURSDAY

Focus area	Equipment	SET 1		SET 2		SET 3		SET 4	
		Weight	Reps	Weight	Reps	Weight	Reps	Weight	Reps

FRIDAY

Focus area	Equipment	SET 1		SET 2		SET 3		SET 4	
		Weight	Reps	Weight	Reps	Weight	Reps	Weight	Reps

SATURDAY

Focus area	Equipment	SET 1		SET 2		SET 3		SET 4	
		Weight	Reps	Weight	Reps	Weight	Reps	Weight	Reps

SUNDAY

Focus area	Equipment	SET 1		SET 2		SET 3		SET 4	
		Weight	Reps	Weight	Reps	Weight	Reps	Weight	Reps

Cardio Training

	Exercise	Time	Distance/resistance	Intensity	Heart rate	Ease	kJ/Cal expended
MONDAY							
							Total:

	Exercise	Time	Distance/resistance	Intensity	Heart rate	Ease	kJ/Cal expended
TUESDAY							
							Total:

	Exercise	Time	Distance/resistance	Intensity	Heart rate	Ease	kJ/Cal expended
WEDNESDAY							
							Total:

	Exercise	Time	Distance/resistance	Intensity	Heart rate	Ease	kJ/Cal expended
THURSDAY							
							Total:

	Exercise	Time	Distance/resistance	Intensity	Heart rate	Ease	kJ/Cal expended
FRIDAY							
							Total:

	Exercise	Time	Distance/resistance	Intensity	Heart rate	Ease	kJ/Cal expended
SATURDAY							
							Total:

	Exercise	Time	Distance/resistance	Intensity	Heart rate	Ease	kJ/Cal expended
SUNDAY							
							Total:

Weekly Total:

Food Diary

MONDAY		kJ/Cal	Fat	Protein	Carbs
Breakfast Time: am/pm					
Lunch Time: am/pm					
Dinner Time: am/pm					
Snacks:					
Coffees/teas:	**Fluid intake:**	**Totals:**			

TUESDAY		kJ/Cal	Fat	Protein	Carbs
Breakfast Time: am/pm					
Lunch Time: am/pm					
Dinner Time: am/pm					
Snacks:					
Coffees/teas:	**Fluid intake:**	**Totals:**			

WEDNESDAY		kJ/Cal	Fat	Protein	Carbs
Breakfast Time: am/pm					
Lunch Time: am/pm					
Dinner Time: am/pm					
Snacks:					
Coffees/teas:	**Fluid intake:**	**Totals:**			

THURSDAY		kJ/Cal	Fat	Protein	Carbs
Breakfast Time: am/pm					
Lunch Time: am/pm					
Dinner Time: am/pm					
Snacks:					
Coffees/teas:	**Fluid intake:**	**Totals:**			

FRIDAY		kJ/Cal	Fat	Protein	Carbs
Breakfast Time: am/pm					
Lunch Time: am/pm					
Dinner Time: am/pm					
Snacks:					
Coffees/teas:	Fluid intake:	Totals:			

SATURDAY		kJ/Cal	Fat	Protein	Carbs
Breakfast Time: am/pm					
Lunch Time: am/pm					
Dinner Time: am/pm					
Snacks:					
Coffees/teas:	Fluid intake:	Totals:			

SUNDAY		kJ/Cal	Fat	Protein	Carbs
Breakfast Time: am/pm					
Lunch Time: am/pm					
Dinner Time: am/pm					
Snacks:					
Coffees/teas:	Fluid intake:	Totals:			

Units of alcohol this week: ⬜   Total alcohol kJ/Cal: ⬜

Vitamins and supplements

Weekly Totals	kJ/Cal	Fat	Protein	Carbs

Weekly Personal Summary

Energy level [1–5] ⬜   Stress level [1–5] ⬜

Hours of sleep ⬜   Sleep quality [1–5] ⬜

Mood [1–5] ⬜   Appetite [1–5] ⬜

kJ/Cal intake

Planned kJ/Cal	
Actual kJ/Cal	

Difference [+/-] ⬜

Weight at start of week ⬜

Weight at end of week ⬜

BMI at start of week ⬜

BMI at end of week ⬜

Injuries or illnesses

Week Beginning

[ ] / [ ] / [ ]

Planned exercise sessions this week

	Exercise	Completed [Y/N]
Monday		
Tuesday		
Wednesday		
Thursday		
Friday		
Saturday		
Sunday		

Strength Training

MONDAY

Focus area	Equipment	SET 1		SET 2		SET 3		SET 4	
		Weight	Reps	Weight	Reps	Weight	Reps	Weight	Reps

TUESDAY

Focus area	Equipment	SET 1		SET 2		SET 3		SET 4	
		Weight	Reps	Weight	Reps	Weight	Reps	Weight	Reps

WEDNESDAY

Focus area	Equipment	SET 1		SET 2		SET 3		SET 4	
		Weight	Reps	Weight	Reps	Weight	Reps	Weight	Reps

THURSDAY

Focus area	Equipment	SET 1		SET 2		SET 3		SET 4	
		Weight	Reps	Weight	Reps	Weight	Reps	Weight	Reps

FRIDAY

Focus area	Equipment	SET 1		SET 2		SET 3		SET 4	
		Weight	Reps	Weight	Reps	Weight	Reps	Weight	Reps

SATURDAY

Focus area	Equipment	SET 1		SET 2		SET 3		SET 4	
		Weight	Reps	Weight	Reps	Weight	Reps	Weight	Reps

SUNDAY

Focus area	Equipment	SET 1		SET 2		SET 3		SET 4	
		Weight	Reps	Weight	Reps	Weight	Reps	Weight	Reps

Cardio Training

MONDAY	Exercise	Time	Distance/resistance	Intensity	Heart rate	Ease	kJ/Cal expended
							Total:

TUESDAY	Exercise	Time	Distance/resistance	Intensity	Heart rate	Ease	kJ/Cal expended
							Total:

WEDNESDAY	Exercise	Time	Distance/resistance	Intensity	Heart rate	Ease	kJ/Cal expended
							Total:

THURSDAY	Exercise	Time	Distance/resistance	Intensity	Heart rate	Ease	kJ/Cal expended
							Total:

FRIDAY	Exercise	Time	Distance/resistance	Intensity	Heart rate	Ease	kJ/Cal expended
							Total:

SATURDAY	Exercise	Time	Distance/resistance	Intensity	Heart rate	Ease	kJ/Cal expended
							Total:

SUNDAY	Exercise	Time	Distance/resistance	Intensity	Heart rate	Ease	kJ/Cal expended
							Total:

Weekly Total:

Food Diary

MONDAY		kJ/Cal	Fat	Protein	Carbs
Breakfast Time: am/pm					
Lunch Time: am/pm					
Dinner Time: am/pm					
Snacks:					
Coffees/teas:	**Fluid intake:**	**Totals:**			

TUESDAY		kJ/Cal	Fat	Protein	Carbs
Breakfast Time: am/pm					
Lunch Time: am/pm					
Dinner Time: am/pm					
Snacks:					
Coffees/teas:	**Fluid intake:**	**Totals:**			

WEDNESDAY		kJ/Cal	Fat	Protein	Carbs
Breakfast Time: am/pm					
Lunch Time: am/pm					
Dinner TIme: am/pm					
Snacks:					
Coffees/teas:	**Fluid intake:**	**Totals:**			

THURSDAY		kJ/Cal	Fat	Protein	Carbs
Breakfast Time: am/pm					
Lunch Time: am/pm					
Dinner Time: am/pm					
Snacks:					
Coffees/teas:	**Fluid intake:**	**Totals:**			

FRIDAY			kJ/Cal	Fat	Protein	Carbs
Breakfast Time: am/pm						
Lunch Time: am/pm						
Dinner Time: am/pm						
Snacks:						
Coffees/teas:	Fluid intake:	Totals:				

SATURDAY			kJ/Cal	Fat	Protein	Carbs
Breakfast Time: am/pm						
Lunch Time: am/pm						
Dinner Time: am/pm						
Snacks:						
Coffees/teas:	Fluid intake:	Totals:				

SUNDAY			kJ/Cal	Fat	Protein	Carbs
Breakfast Time: am/pm						
Lunch Time: am/pm						
Dinner Time: am/pm						
Snacks:						
Coffees/teas:	Fluid intake:	Totals:				

Units of alcohol this week: ▢   Total alcohol kJ/Cal: ▢

Vitamins and supplements

Weekly Totals	kJ/Cal	Fat	Protein	Carbs

Weekly Personal Summary

Energy level [1–5] ▢   Stress level [1–5] ▢

kJ/Cal intake
| Planned kJ/Cal | |
| Actual kJ/Cal | |
Difference [+/-] ▢

Hours of sleep ▢   Sleep quality [1–5] ▢

Mood [1–5] ▢   Appetite [1–5] ▢

Weight at start of week ▢
Weight at end of week ▢
BMI at start of week ▢
BMI at end of week ▢

Injuries or illnesses ▢

Week Beginning

[___ / ___ / ___]

Strength Training

Planned exercise sessions this week

	Exercise	Completed [Y/N]
Monday		
Tuesday		
Wednesday		
Thursday		
Friday		
Saturday		
Sunday		

MONDAY

Focus area	Equipment	SET 1		SET 2		SET 3		SET 4	
		Weight	Reps	Weight	Reps	Weight	Reps	Weight	Reps

TUESDAY

Focus area	Equipment	SET 1		SET 2		SET 3		SET 4	
		Weight	Reps	Weight	Reps	Weight	Reps	Weight	Reps

WEDNESDAY

Focus area	Equipment	SET 1		SET 2		SET 3		SET 4	
		Weight	Reps	Weight	Reps	Weight	Reps	Weight	Reps

THURSDAY

Focus area	Equipment	SET 1		SET 2		SET 3		SET 4	
		Weight	Reps	Weight	Reps	Weight	Reps	Weight	Reps

FRIDAY

Focus area	Equipment	SET 1		SET 2		SET 3		SET 4	
		Weight	Reps	Weight	Reps	Weight	Reps	Weight	Reps

SATURDAY

Focus area	Equipment	SET 1		SET 2		SET 3		SET 4	
		Weight	Reps	Weight	Reps	Weight	Reps	Weight	Reps

SUNDAY

Focus area	Equipment	SET 1		SET 2		SET 3		SET 4	
		Weight	Reps	Weight	Reps	Weight	Reps	Weight	Reps

Cardio Training

	Exercise	Time	Distance/resistance	Intensity	Heart rate	Ease	kJ/Cal expended
MONDAY							
							Total:

	Exercise	Time	Distance/resistance	Intensity	Heart rate	Ease	kJ/Cal expended
TUESDAY							
							Total:

	Exercise	Time	Distance/resistance	Intensity	Heart rate	Ease	kJ/Cal expended
WEDNESDAY							
							Total:

	Exercise	Time	Distance/resistance	Intensity	Heart rate	Ease	kJ/Cal expended
THURSDAY							
							Total:

	Exercise	Time	Distance/resistance	Intensity	Heart rate	Ease	kJ/Cal expended
FRIDAY							
							Total:

	Exercise	Time	Distance/resistance	Intensity	Heart rate	Ease	kJ/Cal expended
SATURDAY							
							Total:

	Exercise	Time	Distance/resistance	Intensity	Heart rate	Ease	kJ/Cal expended
SUNDAY							
							Total:

Weekly Total:

Food Diary

MONDAY		kJ/Cal	Fat	Protein	Carbs
Breakfast Time: am/pm					
Lunch Time: am/pm					
Dinner Time: am/pm					
Snacks:					
Coffees/teas:	Fluid intake:	Totals:			

TUESDAY		kJ/Cal	Fat	Protein	Carbs
Breakfast Time: am/pm					
Lunch Time: am/pm					
Dinner Time: am/pm					
Snacks:					
Coffees/teas:	Fluid intake:	Totals:			

WEDNESDAY		kJ/Cal	Fat	Protein	Carbs
Breakfast Time: am/pm					
Lunch Time: am/pm					
Dinner Time: am/pm					
Snacks:					
Coffees/teas:	Fluid intake:	Totals:			

THURSDAY		kJ/Cal	Fat	Protein	Carbs
Breakfast Time: am/pm					
Lunch Time: am/pm					
Dinner Time: am/pm					
Snacks:					
Coffees/teas:	Fluid intake:	Totals:			

FRIDAY		kJ/Cal	Fat	Protein	Carbs
Breakfast Time: am/pm					
Lunch Time: am/pm					
Dinner Time: am/pm					
Snacks:					
Coffees/teas:	Fluid intake:	Totals:			

SATURDAY		kJ/Cal	Fat	Protein	Carbs
Breakfast Time: am/pm					
Lunch Time: am/pm					
Dinner Time: am/pm					
Snacks:					
Coffees/teas:	Fluid intake:	Totals:			

SUNDAY		kJ/Cal	Fat	Protein	Carbs
Breakfast Time: am/pm					
Lunch Time: am/pm					
Dinner Time: am/pm					
Snacks:					
Coffees/teas:	Fluid intake:	Totals:			

Units of alcohol this week: ☐   Total alcohol kJ/Cal: ☐

Vitamins and supplements

Weekly Totals	kJ/Cal	Fat	Protein	Carbs

Weekly Personal Summary

Energy level [1–5] ☐   Stress level [1–5] ☐

Hours of sleep ☐   Sleep quality [1–5] ☐

Mood [1–5] ☐   Appetite [1–5] ☐

kJ/Cal intake

Planned kJ/Cal	
Actual kJ/Cal	

Difference [+/-] ☐

Weight at start of week ☐

Weight at end of week ☐

BMI at start of week ☐

BMI at end of week ☐

Injuries or illnesses ☐

Week Beginning

/ /

Planned exercise sessions this week

	Exercise	Completed [Y/N]
Monday		
Tuesday		
Wednesday		
Thursday		
Friday		
Saturday		
Sunday		

Strength Training

MONDAY

Focus area	Equipment	SET 1		SET 2		SET 3		SET 4	
		Weight	Reps	Weight	Reps	Weight	Reps	Weight	Reps

TUESDAY

Focus area	Equipment	SET 1		SET 2		SET 3		SET 4	
		Weight	Reps	Weight	Reps	Weight	Reps	Weight	Reps

WEDNESDAY

Focus area	Equipment	SET 1		SET 2		SET 3		SET 4	
		Weight	Reps	Weight	Reps	Weight	Reps	Weight	Reps

THURSDAY

Focus area	Equipment	SET 1		SET 2		SET 3		SET 4	
		Weight	Reps	Weight	Reps	Weight	Reps	Weight	Reps

FRIDAY

Focus area	Equipment	SET 1		SET 2		SET 3		SET 4	
		Weight	Reps	Weight	Reps	Weight	Reps	Weight	Reps

SATURDAY

Focus area	Equipment	SET 1		SET 2		SET 3		SET 4	
		Weight	Reps	Weight	Reps	Weight	Reps	Weight	Reps

SUNDAY

Focus area	Equipment	SET 1		SET 2		SET 3		SET 4	
		Weight	Reps	Weight	Reps	Weight	Reps	Weight	Reps

Cardio Training

MONDAY	Exercise	Time	Distance/resistance	Intensity	Heart rate	Ease	kJ/Cal expended
							Total:

TUESDAY	Exercise	Time	Distance/resistance	Intensity	Heart rate	Ease	kJ/Cal expended
							Total:

WEDNESDAY	Exercise	Time	Distance/resistance	Intensity	Heart rate	Ease	kJ/Cal expended
							Total:

THURSDAY	Exercise	Time	Distance/resistance	Intensity	Heart rate	Ease	kJ/Cal expended
							Total:

FRIDAY	Exercise	Time	Distance/resistance	Intensity	Heart rate	Ease	kJ/Cal expended
							Total:

SATURDAY	Exercise	Time	Distance/resistance	Intensity	Heart rate	Ease	kJ/Cal expended
							Total:

SUNDAY	Exercise	Time	Distance/resistance	Intensity	Heart rate	Ease	kJ/Cal expended
							Total:

Weekly Total:

Food Diary

MONDAY		kJ/Cal	Fat	Protein	Carbs
Breakfast Time: am/pm					
Lunch Time: am/pm					
Dinner Time: am/pm					
Snacks:					
Coffees/teas:	Fluid intake: Totals:				

TUESDAY		kJ/Cal	Fat	Protein	Carbs
Breakfast Time: am/pm					
Lunch Time: am/pm					
Dinner Time: am/pm					
Snacks:					
Coffees/teas:	Fluid intake: Totals:				

WEDNESDAY		kJ/Cal	Fat	Protein	Carbs
Breakfast Time: am/pm					
Lunch Time: am/pm					
Dinner Time: am/pm					
Snacks:					
Coffees/teas:	Fluid intake: Totals:				

THURSDAY		kJ/Cal	Fat	Protein	Carbs
Breakfast Time: am/pm					
Lunch Time: am/pm					
Dinner Time: am/pm					
Snacks:					
Coffees/teas:	Fluid intake: Totals:				

FRIDAY		kJ/Cal	Fat	Protein	Carbs
Breakfast Time: am/pm					
Lunch Time: am/pm					
Dinner Time: am/pm					
Snacks:					
Coffees/teas:	Fluid intake:	Totals:			

SATURDAY		kJ/Cal	Fat	Protein	Carbs
Breakfast Time: am/pm					
Lunch Time: am/pm					
Dinner Time: am/pm					
Snacks:					
Coffees/teas:	Fluid intake:	Totals:			

SUNDAY		kJ/Cal	Fat	Protein	Carbs
Breakfast Time: am/pm					
Lunch Time: am/pm					
Dinner Time: am/pm					
Snacks:					
Coffees/teas:	Fluid intake:	Totals:			

Units of alcohol this week: [   ]   Total alcohol kJ/Cal: [   ]

Vitamins and supplements

Weekly Totals	kJ/Cal	Fat	Protein	Carbs

Weekly Personal Summary

Energy level [ ] 1–5   Stress level [ ] 1–5

kJ/Cal intake

| Planned kJ/Cal | |
| Actual kJ/Cal | |

Difference [+/-] [   ]

Hours of sleep [ ]   Sleep quality [ ] 1–5

Mood [ ] 1–5   Appetite [ ] 1–5

Weight at start of week [   ]
Weight at end of week [   ]
BMI at start of week [   ]
BMI at end of week [   ]

Injuries or illnesses [   ]

Week Beginning

[/   /   ]

Planned exercise sessions this week

	Exercise	Completed [Y/N]
Monday		
Tuesday		
Wednesday		
Thursday		
Friday		
Saturday		
Sunday		

Strength Training

MONDAY

Focus area	Equipment	SET 1		SET 2		SET 3		SET 4	
		Weight	Reps	Weight	Reps	Weight	Reps	Weight	Reps

TUESDAY

Focus area	Equipment	SET 1		SET 2		SET 3		SET 4	
		Weight	Reps	Weight	Reps	Weight	Reps	Weight	Reps

WEDNESDAY

Focus area	Equipment	SET 1		SET 2		SET 3		SET 4	
		Weight	Reps	Weight	Reps	Weight	Reps	Weight	Reps

THURSDAY

Focus area	Equipment	SET 1		SET 2		SET 3		SET 4	
		Weight	Reps	Weight	Reps	Weight	Reps	Weight	Reps

FRIDAY

Focus area	Equipment	SET 1		SET 2		SET 3		SET 4	
		Weight	Reps	Weight	Reps	Weight	Reps	Weight	Reps

SATURDAY

Focus area	Equipment	SET 1		SET 2		SET 3		SET 4	
		Weight	Reps	Weight	Reps	Weight	Reps	Weight	Reps

SUNDAY

Focus area	Equipment	SET 1		SET 2		SET 3		SET 4	
		Weight	Reps	Weight	Reps	Weight	Reps	Weight	Reps

Cardio Training

	Exercise	Time	Distance/resistance	Intensity	Heart rate	Ease	kJ/Cal expended
MONDAY							
							Total:

	Exercise	Time	Distance/resistance	Intensity	Heart rate	Ease	kJ/Cal expended
TUESDAY							
							Total:

	Exercise	Time	Distance/resistance	Intensity	Heart rate	Ease	kJ/Cal expended
WEDNESDAY							
							Total:

	Exercise	Time	Distance/resistance	Intensity	Heart rate	Ease	kJ/Cal expended
THURSDAY							
							Total:

	Exercise	Time	Distance/resistance	Intensity	Heart rate	Ease	kJ/Cal expended
FRIDAY							
							Total:

	Exercise	Time	Distance/resistance	Intensity	Heart rate	Ease	kJ/Cal expended
SATURDAY							
							Total:

	Exercise	Time	Distance/resistance	Intensity	Heart rate	Ease	kJ/Cal expended
SUNDAY							
							Total:

Weekly Total:

Food Diary

MONDAY		kJ/Cal	Fat	Protein	Carbs
Breakfast Time: am/pm					
Lunch Time: am/pm					
Dinner Time: am/pm					
Snacks:					
Coffees/teas:	**Fluid intake:**	**Totals:**			

TUESDAY		kJ/Cal	Fat	Protein	Carbs
Breakfast Time: am/pm					
Lunch Time: am/pm					
Dinner Time: am/pm					
Snacks:					
Coffees/teas:	**Fluid intake:**	**Totals:**			

WEDNESDAY		kJ/Cal	Fat	Protein	Carbs
Breakfast Time: am/pm					
Lunch Time: am/pm					
Dinner Time: am/pm					
Snacks:					
Coffees/teas:	**Fluid intake:**	**Totals:**			

THURSDAY		kJ/Cal	Fat	Protein	Carbs
Breakfast Time: am/pm					
Lunch Time: am/pm					
Dinner Time: am/pm					
Snacks:					
Coffees/teas:	**Fluid intake:**	**Totals:**			

FRIDAY			kJ/Cal	Fat	Protein	Carbs
Breakfast Time: am/pm						
Lunch Time: am/pm						
Dinner Time: am/pm						
Snacks:						
Coffees/teas:	Fluid intake:	Totals:				

SATURDAY			kJ/Cal	Fat	Protein	Carbs
Breakfast Time: am/pm						
Lunch Time: am/pm						
Dinner Time: am/pm						
Snacks:						
Coffees/teas:	Fluid intake:	Totals:				

SUNDAY			kJ/Cal	Fat	Protein	Carbs
Breakfast Time: am/pm						
Lunch Time: am/pm						
Dinner Time: am/pm						
Snacks:						
Coffees/teas:	Fluid intake:	Totals:				

Units of alcohol this week: [   ]   Total alcohol kJ/Cal: [   ]

Vitamins and supplements

Weekly Totals	kJ/Cal	Fat	Protein	Carbs

Weekly Personal Summary

Energy level [ ] (1–5)   Stress level [ ] (1–5)

Hours of sleep [ ]   Sleep quality [ ] (1–5)

Mood [ ] (1–5)   Appetite [ ] (1–5)

kJ/Cal intake

Planned kJ/Cal	[ ]
Actual kJ/Cal	[ ]

Difference [+/-] [   ]

Weight at start of week [   ]

Weight at end of week [   ]

BMI at start of week [   ]

BMI at end of week [   ]

Injuries or illnesses [   ]

Week Beginning

/ /

Planned exercise sessions this week

	Exercise	Completed [Y/N]
Monday		
Tuesday		
Wednesday		
Thursday		
Friday		
Saturday		
Sunday		

Strength Training

MONDAY

Focus area	Equipment	SET 1		SET 2		SET 3		SET 4	
		Weight	Reps	Weight	Reps	Weight	Reps	Weight	Reps

TUESDAY

Focus area	Equipment	SET 1		SET 2		SET 3		SET 4	
		Weight	Reps	Weight	Reps	Weight	Reps	Weight	Reps

WEDNESDAY

Focus area	Equipment	SET 1		SET 2		SET 3		SET 4	
		Weight	Reps	Weight	Reps	Weight	Reps	Weight	Reps

THURSDAY

Focus area	Equipment	SET 1		SET 2		SET 3		SET 4	
		Weight	Reps	Weight	Reps	Weight	Reps	Weight	Reps

FRIDAY

Focus area	Equipment	SET 1		SET 2		SET 3		SET 4	
		Weight	Reps	Weight	Reps	Weight	Reps	Weight	Reps

SATURDAY

Focus area	Equipment	SET 1		SET 2		SET 3		SET 4	
		Weight	Reps	Weight	Reps	Weight	Reps	Weight	Reps

SUNDAY

Focus area	Equipment	SET 1		SET 2		SET 3		SET 4	
		Weight	Reps	Weight	Reps	Weight	Reps	Weight	Reps

Cardio Training

	Exercise	Time	Distance/resistance	Intensity	Heart rate	Ease	kJ/Cal expended
MONDAY							
							Total:

	Exercise	Time	Distance/resistance	Intensity	Heart rate	Ease	kJ/Cal expended
TUESDAY							
							Total:

	Exercise	Time	Distance/resistance	Intensity	Heart rate	Ease	kJ/Cal expended
WEDNESDAY							
							Total:

	Exercise	Time	Distance/resistance	Intensity	Heart rate	Ease	kJ/Cal expended
THURSDAY							
							Total:

	Exercise	Time	Distance/resistance	Intensity	Heart rate	Ease	kJ/Cal expended
FRIDAY							
							Total:

	Exercise	Time	Distance/resistance	Intensity	Heart rate	Ease	kJ/Cal expended
SATURDAY							
							Total:

	Exercise	Time	Distance/resistance	Intensity	Heart rate	Ease	kJ/Cal expended
SUNDAY							
							Total:
							Weekly Total:

Food Diary

MONDAY		kJ/Cal	Fat	Protein	Carbs
Breakfast Time: am/pm					
Lunch Time: am/pm					
Dinner Time: am/pm					
Snacks:					
Coffees/teas:	Fluid intake:	Totals:			

TUESDAY		kJ/Cal	Fat	Protein	Carbs
Breakfast Time: am/pm					
Lunch Time: am/pm					
Dinner Time: am/pm					
Snacks:					
Coffees/teas:	Fluid intake:	Totals:			

WEDNESDAY		kJ/Cal	Fat	Protein	Carbs
Breakfast Time: am/pm					
Lunch Time: am/pm					
Dinner Time: am/pm					
Snacks:					
Coffees/teas:	Fluid intake:	Totals:			

THURSDAY		kJ/Cal	Fat	Protein	Carbs
Breakfast Time: am/pm					
Lunch Time: am/pm					
Dinner Time: am/pm					
Snacks:					
Coffees/teas:	Fluid intake:	Totals:			

FRIDAY		kJ/Cal	Fat	Protein	Carbs
Breakfast Time: am/pm					
Lunch Time: am/pm					
Dinner Time: am/pm					
Snacks:					
Coffees/teas:	Fluid intake:	Totals:			

SATURDAY		kJ/Cal	Fat	Protein	Carbs
Breakfast Time: am/pm					
Lunch Time: am/pm					
Dinner Time: am/pm					
Snacks:					
Coffees/teas:	Fluid intake:	Totals:			

SUNDAY		kJ/Cal	Fat	Protein	Carbs
Breakfast Time: am/pm					
Lunch Time: am/pm					
Dinner Time: am/pm					
Snacks:					
Coffees/teas:	Fluid intake:	Totals:			

Units of alcohol this week: [ ]   Total alcohol kJ/Cal: [ ]

Vitamins and supplements

Weekly Totals	kJ/Cal	Fat	Protein	Carbs

Weekly Personal Summary

Energy level 1-5 [ ]   Stress level 1-5 [ ]

Hours of sleep [ ]   Sleep quality 1-5 [ ]

Mood 1-5 [ ]   Appetite 1-5 [ ]

kJ/Cal intake

| Planned kJ/Cal | |
| Actual kJ/Cal | |

Difference [+/-] [ ]

Weight at start of week [ ]

Weight at end of week [ ]

BMI at start of week [ ]

BMI at end of week [ ]

Injuries or illnesses [ ]

Week Beginning

[ ] / [ ] / [ ]

Planned exercise sessions this week

	Exercise	Completed [Y/N]
Monday		
Tuesday		
Wednesday		
Thursday		
Friday		
Saturday		
Sunday		

Strength Training

MONDAY

Focus area	Equipment	SET 1 Weight	SET 1 Reps	SET 2 Weight	SET 2 Reps	SET 3 Weight	SET 3 Reps	SET 4 Weight	SET 4 Reps

TUESDAY

Focus area	Equipment	SET 1 Weight	SET 1 Reps	SET 2 Weight	SET 2 Reps	SET 3 Weight	SET 3 Reps	SET 4 Weight	SET 4 Reps

WEDNESDAY

Focus area	Equipment	SET 1 Weight	SET 1 Reps	SET 2 Weight	SET 2 Reps	SET 3 Weight	SET 3 Reps	SET 4 Weight	SET 4 Reps

THURSDAY

Focus area	Equipment	SET 1 Weight	SET 1 Reps	SET 2 Weight	SET 2 Reps	SET 3 Weight	SET 3 Reps	SET 4 Weight	SET 4 Reps

FRIDAY

Focus area	Equipment	SET 1 Weight	SET 1 Reps	SET 2 Weight	SET 2 Reps	SET 3 Weight	SET 3 Reps	SET 4 Weight	SET 4 Reps

SATURDAY

Focus area	Equipment	SET 1 Weight	SET 1 Reps	SET 2 Weight	SET 2 Reps	SET 3 Weight	SET 3 Reps	SET 4 Weight	SET 4 Reps

SUNDAY

Focus area	Equipment	SET 1 Weight	SET 1 Reps	SET 2 Weight	SET 2 Reps	SET 3 Weight	SET 3 Reps	SET 4 Weight	SET 4 Reps

Cardio Training

	Exercise	Time	Distance/resistance	Intensity	Heart rate	Ease	kJ/Cal expended
MONDAY							
							Total:

	Exercise	Time	Distance/resistance	Intensity	Heart rate	Ease	kJ/Cal expended
TUESDAY							
							Total:

	Exercise	Time	Distance/resistance	Intensity	Heart rate	Ease	kJ/Cal expended
WEDNESDAY							
							Total:

	Exercise	Time	Distance/resistance	Intensity	Heart rate	Ease	kJ/Cal expended
THURSDAY							
							Total:

	Exercise	Time	Distance/resistance	Intensity	Heart rate	Ease	kJ/Cal expended
FRIDAY							
							Total:

	Exercise	Time	Distance/resistance	Intensity	Heart rate	Ease	kJ/Cal expended
SATURDAY							
							Total:

	Exercise	Time	Distance/resistance	Intensity	Heart rate	Ease	kJ/Cal expended
SUNDAY							
							Total:
							Weekly Total:

Food Diary

MONDAY		kJ/Cal	Fat	Protein	Carbs
Breakfast Time: am/pm					
Lunch Time: am/pm					
Dinner Time: am/pm					
Snacks:					
Coffees/teas:	Fluid intake:	Totals:			

TUESDAY		kJ/Cal	Fat	Protein	Carbs
Breakfast Time: am/pm					
Lunch Time: am/pm					
Dinner Time: am/pm					
Snacks:					
Coffees/teas:	Fluid intake:	Totals:			

WEDNESDAY		kJ/Cal	Fat	Protein	Carbs
Breakfast Time: am/pm					
Lunch Time: am/pm					
Dinner Time: am/pm					
Snacks:					
Coffees/teas:	Fluid intake:	Totals:			

THURSDAY		kJ/Cal	Fat	Protein	Carbs
Breakfast Time: am/pm					
Lunch Time: am/pm					
Dinner Time: am/pm					
Snacks:					
Coffees/teas:	Fluid intake:	Totals:			

FRIDAY			kJ/Cal	Fat	Protein	Carbs
Breakfast Time: am/pm						
Lunch Time: am/pm						
Dinner Time: am/pm						
Snacks:						
Coffees/teas:	Fluid intake:	Totals:				

SATURDAY			kJ/Cal	Fat	Protein	Carbs
Breakfast Time: am/pm						
Lunch Time: am/pm						
Dinner Time: am/pm						
Snacks:						
Coffees/teas:	Fluid intake:	Totals:				

SUNDAY			kJ/Cal	Fat	Protein	Carbs
Breakfast Time: am/pm						
Lunch Time: am/pm						
Dinner Time: am/pm						
Snacks:						
Coffees/teas:	Fluid intake:	Totals:				

Units of alcohol this week: Total alcohol kJ/Cal:

Vitamins and supplements

Weekly Totals	kJ/Cal	Fat	Protein	Carbs

Weekly Personal Summary

Energy level [1–5] Stress level [1–5]

kJ/Cal intake

| Planned kJ/Cal | |
| Actual kJ/Cal | |

Difference [+/-]

Hours of sleep Sleep quality [1–5]

Mood [1–5] Appetite [1–5]

Injuries or illnesses

Weight at start of week

Weight at end of week

BMI at start of week

BMI at end of week

Week Beginning

[ ] / [ ] / [ ]

Planned exercise sessions this week

	Exercise	Completed [Y/N]
Monday		
Tuesday		
Wednesday		
Thursday		
Friday		
Saturday		
Sunday		

Strength Training

MONDAY

Focus area	Equipment	SET 1		SET 2		SET 3		SET 4	
		Weight	Reps	Weight	Reps	Weight	Reps	Weight	Reps

TUESDAY

Focus area	Equipment	SET 1		SET 2		SET 3		SET 4	
		Weight	Reps	Weight	Reps	Weight	Reps	Weight	Reps

WEDNESDAY

Focus area	Equipment	SET 1		SET 2		SET 3		SET 4	
		Weight	Reps	Weight	Reps	Weight	Reps	Weight	Reps

THURSDAY

Focus area	Equipment	SET 1		SET 2		SET 3		SET 4	
		Weight	Reps	Weight	Reps	Weight	Reps	Weight	Reps

FRIDAY

Focus area	Equipment	SET 1		SET 2		SET 3		SET 4	
		Weight	Reps	Weight	Reps	Weight	Reps	Weight	Reps

SATURDAY

Focus area	Equipment	SET 1		SET 2		SET 3		SET 4	
		Weight	Reps	Weight	Reps	Weight	Reps	Weight	Reps

SUNDAY

Focus area	Equipment	SET 1		SET 2		SET 3		SET 4	
		Weight	Reps	Weight	Reps	Weight	Reps	Weight	Reps

Cardio Training

MONDAY

	Exercise	Time	Distance/resistance	Intensity	Heart rate	Ease	kJ/Cal expended
							Total:

TUESDAY

	Exercise	Time	Distance/resistance	Intensity	Heart rate	Ease	kJ/Cal expended
							Total:

WEDNESDAY

	Exercise	Time	Distance/resistance	Intensity	Heart rate	Ease	kJ/Cal expended
							Total:

THURSDAY

	Exercise	Time	Distance/resistance	Intensity	Heart rate	Ease	kJ/Cal expended
							Total:

FRIDAY

	Exercise	Time	Distance/resistance	Intensity	Heart rate	Ease	kJ/Cal expended
							Total:

SATURDAY

	Exercise	Time	Distance/resistance	Intensity	Heart rate	Ease	kJ/Cal expended
							Total:

SUNDAY

	Exercise	Time	Distance/resistance	Intensity	Heart rate	Ease	kJ/Cal expended
							Total:

Weekly Total:

Food Diary

MONDAY		kJ/Cal	Fat	Protein	Carbs
Breakfast Time: am/pm					
Lunch Time: am/pm					
Dinner Time: am/pm					
Snacks:					
Coffees/teas:	Fluid intake:	Totals:			

TUESDAY		kJ/Cal	Fat	Protein	Carbs
Breakfast Time: am/pm					
Lunch Time: am/pm					
Dinner Time: am/pm					
Snacks:					
Coffees/teas:	Fluid intake:	Totals:			

WEDNESDAY		kJ/Cal	Fat	Protein	Carbs
Breakfast Time: am/pm					
Lunch Time: am/pm					
Dinner Time: am/pm					
Snacks:					
Coffees/teas:	Fluid intake:	Totals:			

THURSDAY		kJ/Cal	Fat	Protein	Carbs
Breakfast Time: am/pm					
Lunch Time: am/pm					
Dinner Time: am/pm					
Snacks:					
Coffees/teas:	Fluid intake:	Totals:			

FRIDAY			kJ/Cal	Fat	Protein	Carbs
Breakfast Time: am/pm						
Lunch Time: am/pm						
Dinner Time: am/pm						
Snacks:						
Coffees/teas:	Fluid intake:	Totals:				

SATURDAY			kJ/Cal	Fat	Protein	Carbs
Breakfast Time: am/pm						
Lunch Time: am/pm						
Dinner Time: am/pm						
Snacks:						
Coffees/teas:	Fluid intake:	Totals:				

SUNDAY			kJ/Cal	Fat	Protein	Carbs
Breakfast Time: am/pm						
Lunch Time: am/pm						
Dinner Time: am/pm						
Snacks:						
Coffees/teas:	Fluid intake:	Totals:				

Units of alcohol this week: ___   Total alcohol kJ/Cal: ___

Vitamins and supplements

Weekly Totals	kJ/Cal	Fat	Protein	Carbs

Weekly Personal Summary

Energy level 1–5 ___   Stress level 1–5 ___

Hours of sleep ___   Sleep quality 1–5 ___

Mood 1–5 ___   Appetite 1–5 ___

kJ/Cal intake

Planned kJ/Cal	
Actual kJ/Cal	
Difference [+/-]	

Weight at start of week ___
Weight at end of week ___
BMI at start of week ___
BMI at end of week ___

Injuries or illnesses ___

Week Beginning

[/ /]

	Exercise	Completed [Y/N]
Monday		
Tuesday		
Wednesday		
Thursday		
Friday		
Saturday		
Sunday		

Strength Training

MONDAY

Focus area	Equipment	SET 1		SET 2		SET 3		SET 4	
		Weight	Reps	Weight	Reps	Weight	Reps	Weight	Reps

TUESDAY

Focus area	Equipment	SET 1		SET 2		SET 3		SET 4	
		Weight	Reps	Weight	Reps	Weight	Reps	Weight	Reps

WEDNESDAY

Focus area	Equipment	SET 1		SET 2		SET 3		SET 4	
		Weight	Reps	Weight	Reps	Weight	Reps	Weight	Reps

THURSDAY

Focus area	Equipment	SET 1		SET 2		SET 3		SET 4	
		Weight	Reps	Weight	Reps	Weight	Reps	Weight	Reps

FRIDAY

Focus area	Equipment	SET 1		SET 2		SET 3		SET 4	
		Weight	Reps	Weight	Reps	Weight	Reps	Weight	Reps

SATURDAY

Focus area	Equipment	SET 1		SET 2		SET 3		SET 4	
		Weight	Reps	Weight	Reps	Weight	Reps	Weight	Reps

SUNDAY

Focus area	Equipment	SET 1		SET 2		SET 3		SET 4	
		Weight	Reps	Weight	Reps	Weight	Reps	Weight	Reps

Cardio Training

	Exercise	Time	Distance/resistance	Intensity	Heart rate	Ease	kJ/Cal expended
MONDAY							
							Total:

	Exercise	Time	Distance/resistance	Intensity	Heart rate	Ease	kJ/Cal expended
TUESDAY							
							Total:

	Exercise	Time	Distance/resistance	Intensity	Heart rate	Ease	kJ/Cal expended
WEDNESDAY							
							Total:

	Exercise	Time	Distance/resistance	Intensity	Heart rate	Ease	kJ/Cal expended
THURSDAY							
							Total:

	Exercise	Time	Distance/resistance	Intensity	Heart rate	Ease	kJ/Cal expended
FRIDAY							
							Total:

	Exercise	Time	Distance/resistance	Intensity	Heart rate	Ease	kJ/Cal expended
SATURDAY							
							Total:

	Exercise	Time	Distance/resistance	Intensity	Heart rate	Ease	kJ/Cal expended
SUNDAY							
							Total:

Weekly Total:

Food Diary

MONDAY		kJ/Cal	Fat	Protein	Carbs
Breakfast Time: am/pm					
Lunch Time: am/pm					
Dinner Time: am/pm					
Snacks:					
Coffees/teas:	Fluid intake:	Totals:			

TUESDAY		kJ/Cal	Fat	Protein	Carbs
Breakfast Time: am/pm					
Lunch Time: am/pm					
Dinner Time: am/pm					
Snacks:					
Coffees/teas:	Fluid intake:	Totals:			

WEDNESDAY		kJ/Cal	Fat	Protein	Carbs
Breakfast Time: am/pm					
Lunch Time: am/pm					
Dinner TIme: am/pm					
Snacks:					
Coffees/teas:	Fluid intake:	Totals:			

THURSDAY		kJ/Cal	Fat	Protein	Carbs
Breakfast Time: am/pm					
Lunch Time: am/pm					
Dinner Time: am/pm					
Snacks:					
Coffees/teas:	Fluid intake:	Totals:			

FRIDAY		kJ/Cal	Fat	Protein	Carbs
Breakfast Time: am/pm					
Lunch Time: am/pm					
Dinner Time: am/pm					
Snacks:					
Coffees/teas:	Fluid intake:	Totals:			

SATURDAY		kJ/Cal	Fat	Protein	Carbs
Breakfast Time: am/pm					
Lunch Time: am/pm					
Dinner Time: am/pm					
Snacks:					
Coffees/teas:	Fluid intake:	Totals:			

SUNDAY		kJ/Cal	Fat	Protein	Carbs
Breakfast Time: am/pm					
Lunch Time: am/pm					
Dinner Time: am/pm					
Snacks:					
Coffees/teas:	Fluid intake:	Totals:			

Units of alcohol this week: Total alcohol kJ/Cal:

Vitamins and supplements

Weekly Totals	kJ/Cal	Fat	Protein	Carbs

Weekly Personal Summary

Energy level   1–5   Stress level   1–5

Hours of sleep   Sleep quality   1–5

Mood   1–5   Appetite   1–5

kJ/Cal intake

Planned kJ/Cal	
Actual kJ/Cal	
Difference [+/-]	

Weight at start of week

Weight at end of week

BMI at start of week

BMI at end of week

Injuries or illnesses

205

Week Beginning

___ / ___ / ___

Planned exercise sessions this week

	Exercise	Completed [Y/N]
Monday		
Tuesday		
Wednesday		
Thursday		
Friday		
Saturday		
Sunday		

Strength Training

MONDAY

Focus area	Equipment	SET 1		SET 2		SET 3		SET 4	
		Weight	Reps	Weight	Reps	Weight	Reps	Weight	Reps

TUESDAY

Focus area	Equipment	SET 1		SET 2		SET 3		SET 4	
		Weight	Reps	Weight	Reps	Weight	Reps	Weight	Reps

WEDNESDAY

Focus area	Equipment	SET 1		SET 2		SET 3		SET 4	
		Weight	Reps	Weight	Reps	Weight	Reps	Weight	Reps

THURSDAY

Focus area	Equipment	SET 1		SET 2		SET 3		SET 4	
		Weight	Reps	Weight	Reps	Weight	Reps	Weight	Reps

FRIDAY

Focus area	Equipment	SET 1		SET 2		SET 3		SET 4	
		Weight	Reps	Weight	Reps	Weight	Reps	Weight	Reps

SATURDAY

Focus area	Equipment	SET 1		SET 2		SET 3		SET 4	
		Weight	Reps	Weight	Reps	Weight	Reps	Weight	Reps

SUNDAY

Focus area	Equipment	SET 1		SET 2		SET 3		SET 4	
		Weight	Reps	Weight	Reps	Weight	Reps	Weight	Reps

Cardio Training

MONDAY

Exercise	Time	Distance/resistance	Intensity	Heart rate	Ease	kJ/Cal expended
						Total:

TUESDAY

Exercise	Time	Distance/resistance	Intensity	Heart rate	Ease	kJ/Cal expended
						Total:

WEDNESDAY

Exercise	Time	Distance/resistance	Intensity	Heart rate	Ease	kJ/Cal expended
						Total:

THURSDAY

Exercise	Time	Distance/resistance	Intensity	Heart rate	Ease	kJ/Cal expended
						Total:

FRIDAY

Exercise	Time	Distance/resistance	Intensity	Heart rate	Ease	kJ/Cal expended
						Total:

SATURDAY

Exercise	Time	Distance/resistance	Intensity	Heart rate	Ease	kJ/Cal expended
						Total:

SUNDAY

Exercise	Time	Distance/resistance	Intensity	Heart rate	Ease	kJ/Cal expended
						Total:

Weekly Total:

Food Diary

MONDAY		kJ/Cal	Fat	Protein	Carbs
Breakfast Time: am/pm					
Lunch Time: am/pm					
Dinner Time: am/pm					
Snacks:					
Coffees/teas:	Fluid intake: Totals:				

TUESDAY		kJ/Cal	Fat	Protein	Carbs
Breakfast Time: am/pm					
Lunch Time: am/pm					
Dinner Time: am/pm					
Snacks:					
Coffees/teas:	Fluid intake: Totals:				

WEDNESDAY		kJ/Cal	Fat	Protein	Carbs
Breakfast Time: am/pm					
Lunch Time: am/pm					
Dinner Time: am/pm					
Snacks:					
Coffees/teas:	Fluid intake: Totals:				

THURSDAY		kJ/Cal	Fat	Protein	Carbs
Breakfast Time: am/pm					
Lunch Time: am/pm					
Dinner Time: am/pm					
Snacks:					
Coffees/teas:	Fluid intake: Totals:				

FRIDAY			kJ/Cal	Fat	Protein	Carbs
Breakfast Time: am/pm						
Lunch Time: am/pm						
Dinner Time: am/pm						
Snacks:						
Coffees/teas:	Fluid intake:	Totals:				

SATURDAY			kJ/Cal	Fat	Protein	Carbs
Breakfast Time: am/pm						
Lunch Time: am/pm						
Dinner Time: am/pm						
Snacks:						
Coffees/teas:	Fluid intake:	Totals:				

SUNDAY			kJ/Cal	Fat	Protein	Carbs
Breakfast Time: am/pm						
Lunch Time: am/pm						
Dinner Time: am/pm						
Snacks:						
Coffees/teas:	Fluid intake:	Totals:				

Units of alcohol this week: _____   Total alcohol kJ/Cal: _____

Vitamins and supplements

Weekly Totals	kJ/Cal	Fat	Protein	Carbs

Weekly Personal Summary

Energy level [1–5]   Stress level [1–5]

Hours of sleep   Sleep quality [1–5]

Mood [1–5]   Appetite [1–5]

Injuries or illnesses _____

kJ/Cal intake

Planned kJ/Cal _____
Actual kJ/Cal _____
Difference [+/-] _____

Weight at start of week _____
Weight at end of week _____
BMI at start of week _____
BMI at end of week _____

Week Beginning

___ / ___ / ___

Planned exercise sessions this week

	Exercise	Completed [Y/N]
Monday		
Tuesday		
Wednesday		
Thursday		
Friday		
Saturday		
Sunday		

Strength Training

MONDAY

Focus area	Equipment	SET 1		SET 2		SET 3		SET 4	
		Weight	Reps	Weight	Reps	Weight	Reps	Weight	Reps

TUESDAY

Focus area	Equipment	SET 1		SET 2		SET 3		SET 4	
		Weight	Reps	Weight	Reps	Weight	Reps	Weight	Reps

WEDNESDAY

Focus area	Equipment	SET 1		SET 2		SET 3		SET 4	
		Weight	Reps	Weight	Reps	Weight	Reps	Weight	Reps

THURSDAY

Focus area	Equipment	SET 1		SET 2		SET 3		SET 4	
		Weight	Reps	Weight	Reps	Weight	Reps	Weight	Reps

FRIDAY

Focus area	Equipment	SET 1		SET 2		SET 3		SET 4	
		Weight	Reps	Weight	Reps	Weight	Reps	Weight	Reps

SATURDAY

Focus area	Equipment	SET 1		SET 2		SET 3		SET 4	
		Weight	Reps	Weight	Reps	Weight	Reps	Weight	Reps

SUNDAY

Focus area	Equipment	SET 1		SET 2		SET 3		SET 4	
		Weight	Reps	Weight	Reps	Weight	Reps	Weight	Reps

Cardio Training

MONDAY

Exercise	Time	Distance/resistance	Intensity	Heart rate	Ease	kJ/Cal expended
						Total:

TUESDAY

Exercise	Time	Distance/resistance	Intensity	Heart rate	Ease	kJ/Cal expended
						Total:

WEDNESDAY

Exercise	Time	Distance/resistance	Intensity	Heart rate	Ease	kJ/Cal expended
						Total:

THURSDAY

Exercise	Time	Distance/resistance	Intensity	Heart rate	Ease	kJ/Cal expended
						Total:

FRIDAY

Exercise	Time	Distance/resistance	Intensity	Heart rate	Ease	kJ/Cal expended
						Total:

SATURDAY

Exercise	Time	Distance/resistance	Intensity	Heart rate	Ease	kJ/Cal expended
						Total:

SUNDAY

Exercise	Time	Distance/resistance	Intensity	Heart rate	Ease	kJ/Cal expended
						Total:

Weekly Total:

Food Diary

MONDAY		kJ/Cal	Fat	Protein	Carbs
Breakfast Time: am/pm					
Lunch Time: am/pm					
Dinner Time: am/pm					
Snacks:					
Coffees/teas:	Fluid intake:	Totals:			

TUESDAY		kJ/Cal	Fat	Protein	Carbs
Breakfast Time: am/pm					
Lunch Time: am/pm					
Dinner Time: am/pm					
Snacks:					
Coffees/teas:	Fluid intake:	Totals:			

WEDNESDAY		kJ/Cal	Fat	Protein	Carbs
Breakfast Time: am/pm					
Lunch Time: am/pm					
Dinner Time: am/pm					
Snacks:					
Coffees/teas:	Fluid intake:	Totals:			

THURSDAY		kJ/Cal	Fat	Protein	Carbs
Breakfast Time: am/pm					
Lunch Time: am/pm					
Dinner Time: am/pm					
Snacks:					
Coffees/teas:	Fluid intake:	Totals:			

FRIDAY		kJ/Cal	Fat	Protein	Carbs
Breakfast Time: am/pm					
Lunch Time: am/pm					
Dinner Time: am/pm					
Snacks:					
Coffees/teas:	Fluid intake:	Totals:			

SATURDAY		kJ/Cal	Fat	Protein	Carbs
Breakfast Time: am/pm					
Lunch Time: am/pm					
Dinner Time: am/pm					
Snacks:					
Coffees/teas:	Fluid intake:	Totals:			

SUNDAY		kJ/Cal	Fat	Protein	Carbs
Breakfast Time: am/pm					
Lunch Time: am/pm					
Dinner Time: am/pm					
Snacks:					
Coffees/teas:	Fluid intake:	Totals:			

Units of alcohol this week: [   ]   Total alcohol kJ/Cal: [   ]

Vitamins and supplements

Weekly Totals	kJ/Cal	Fat	Protein	Carbs

Weekly Personal Summary

Energy level 1–5 [ ]   Stress level 1–5 [ ]

kJ/Cal intake

Planned kJ/Cal	
Actual kJ/Cal	

Difference [+/-] [   ]

Hours of sleep [   ]   Sleep quality 1–5 [ ]

Mood 1–5 [ ]   Appetite 1–5 [ ]

Weight at start of week [   ]
Weight at end of week [   ]
BMI at start of week [   ]
BMI at end of week [   ]

Injuries or illnesses [   ]

Week Beginning

[ ] / [ ] / [ ]

	Exercise	Completed [Y/N]
Monday		
Tuesday		
Wednesday		
Thursday		
Friday		
Saturday		
Sunday		

Strength Training

MONDAY

Focus area	Equipment	SET 1		SET 2		SET 3		SET 4	
		Weight	Reps	Weight	Reps	Weight	Reps	Weight	Reps

TUESDAY

Focus area	Equipment	SET 1		SET 2		SET 3		SET 4	
		Weight	Reps	Weight	Reps	Weight	Reps	Weight	Reps

WEDNESDAY

Focus area	Equipment	SET 1		SET 2		SET 3		SET 4	
		Weight	Reps	Weight	Reps	Weight	Reps	Weight	Reps

THURSDAY

Focus area	Equipment	SET 1		SET 2		SET 3		SET 4	
		Weight	Reps	Weight	Reps	Weight	Reps	Weight	Reps

FRIDAY

Focus area	Equipment	SET 1		SET 2		SET 3		SET 4	
		Weight	Reps	Weight	Reps	Weight	Reps	Weight	Reps

SATURDAY

Focus area	Equipment	SET 1		SET 2		SET 3		SET 4	
		Weight	Reps	Weight	Reps	Weight	Reps	Weight	Reps

SUNDAY

Focus area	Equipment	SET 1		SET 2		SET 3		SET 4	
		Weight	Reps	Weight	Reps	Weight	Reps	Weight	Reps

Cardio Training

MONDAY	Exercise	Time	Distance/resistance	Intensity	Heart rate	Ease	kJ/Cal expended
							Total:

TUESDAY	Exercise	Time	Distance/resistance	Intensity	Heart rate	Ease	kJ/Cal expended
							Total:

WEDNESDAY	Exercise	Time	Distance/resistance	Intensity	Heart rate	Ease	kJ/Cal expended
							Total:

THURSDAY	Exercise	Time	Distance/resistance	Intensity	Heart rate	Ease	kJ/Cal expended
							Total:

FRIDAY	Exercise	Time	Distance/resistance	Intensity	Heart rate	Ease	kJ/Cal expended
							Total:

SATURDAY	Exercise	Time	Distance/resistance	Intensity	Heart rate	Ease	kJ/Cal expended
							Total:

SUNDAY	Exercise	Time	Distance/resistance	Intensity	Heart rate	Ease	kJ/Cal expended
							Total:

Weekly Total:

Food Diary

MONDAY		kJ/Cal	Fat	Protein	Carbs
Breakfast Time: am/pm					
Lunch Time: am/pm					
Dinner Time: am/pm					
Snacks:					
Coffees/teas:	Fluid intake:	Totals:			

TUESDAY		kJ/Cal	Fat	Protein	Carbs
Breakfast Time: am/pm					
Lunch Time: am/pm					
Dinner Time: am/pm					
Snacks:					
Coffees/teas:	Fluid intake:	Totals:			

WEDNESDAY		kJ/Cal	Fat	Protein	Carbs
Breakfast Time: am/pm					
Lunch Time: am/pm					
Dinner Time: am/pm					
Snacks:					
Coffees/teas:	Fluid intake:	Totals:			

THURSDAY		kJ/Cal	Fat	Protein	Carbs
Breakfast Time: am/pm					
Lunch Time: am/pm					
Dinner Time: am/pm					
Snacks:					
Coffees/teas:	Fluid intake:	Totals:			

FRIDAY			kJ/Cal	Fat	Protein	Carbs
Breakfast Time: am/pm						
Lunch Time: am/pm						
Dinner Time: am/pm						
Snacks:						
Coffees/teas:	Fluid intake:	Totals:				

SATURDAY			kJ/Cal	Fat	Protein	Carbs
Breakfast Time: am/pm						
Lunch Time: am/pm						
Dinner Time: am/pm						
Snacks:						
Coffees/teas:	Fluid intake:	Totals:				

SUNDAY			kJ/Cal	Fat	Protein	Carbs
Breakfast Time: am/pm						
Lunch Time: am/pm						
Dinner Time: am/pm						
Snacks:						
Coffees/teas:	Fluid intake:	Totals:				

Units of alcohol this week: Total alcohol kJ/Cal:

Vitamins and supplements

Weekly Totals	kJ/Cal	Fat	Protein	Carbs

Weekly Personal Summary

Energy level [1–5]   Stress level [1–5]

Hours of sleep   Sleep quality [1–5]

Mood [1–5]   Appetite [1–5]

kJ/Cal intake

Planned kJ/Cal	
Actual kJ/Cal	

Difference [+/-]

Weight at start of week

Weight at end of week

BMI at start of week

BMI at end of week

Injuries or illnesses

Week Beginning

[ ] / [ ] / [ ]

Planned exercise sessions this week

	Exercise	Completed [Y/N]
Monday		
Tuesday		
Wednesday		
Thursday		
Friday		
Saturday		
Sunday		

Strength Training

MONDAY

Focus area	Equipment	SET 1		SET 2		SET 3		SET 4	
		Weight	Reps	Weight	Reps	Weight	Reps	Weight	Reps

TUESDAY

Focus area	Equipment	SET 1		SET 2		SET 3		SET 4	
		Weight	Reps	Weight	Reps	Weight	Reps	Weight	Reps

WEDNESDAY

Focus area	Equipment	SET 1		SET 2		SET 3		SET 4	
		Weight	Reps	Weight	Reps	Weight	Reps	Weight	Reps

THURSDAY

Focus area	Equipment	SET 1		SET 2		SET 3		SET 4	
		Weight	Reps	Weight	Reps	Weight	Reps	Weight	Reps

FRIDAY

Focus area	Equipment	SET 1		SET 2		SET 3		SET 4	
		Weight	Reps	Weight	Reps	Weight	Reps	Weight	Reps

SATURDAY

Focus area	Equipment	SET 1		SET 2		SET 3		SET 4	
		Weight	Reps	Weight	Reps	Weight	Reps	Weight	Reps

SUNDAY

Focus area	Equipment	SET 1		SET 2		SET 3		SET 4	
		Weight	Reps	Weight	Reps	Weight	Reps	Weight	Reps

Cardio Training

	Exercise	Time	Distance/resistance	Intensity	Heart rate	Ease	kJ/Cal expended
MONDAY							
							Total:

	Exercise	Time	Distance/resistance	Intensity	Heart rate	Ease	kJ/Cal expended
TUESDAY							
							Total:

	Exercise	Time	Distance/resistance	Intensity	Heart rate	Ease	kJ/Cal expended
WEDNESDAY							
							Total:

	Exercise	Time	Distance/resistance	Intensity	Heart rate	Ease	kJ/Cal expended
THURSDAY							
							Total:

	Exercise	Time	Distance/resistance	Intensity	Heart rate	Ease	kJ/Cal expended
FRIDAY							
							Total:

	Exercise	Time	Distance/resistance	Intensity	Heart rate	Ease	kJ/Cal expended
SATURDAY							
							Total:

	Exercise	Time	Distance/resistance	Intensity	Heart rate	Ease	kJ/Cal expended
SUNDAY							
							Total:

Weekly Total:

Food Diary

MONDAY		kJ/Cal	Fat	Protein	Carbs
Breakfast Time: am/pm					
Lunch Time: am/pm					
Dinner Time: am/pm					
Snacks:					
Coffees/teas:	Fluid intake:	Totals:			

TUESDAY		kJ/Cal	Fat	Protein	Carbs
Breakfast Time: am/pm					
Lunch Time: am/pm					
Dinner Time: am/pm					
Snacks:					
Coffees/teas:	Fluid intake:	Totals:			

WEDNESDAY		kJ/Cal	Fat	Protein	Carbs
Breakfast Time: am/pm					
Lunch Time: am/pm					
Dinner Time: am/pm					
Snacks:					
Coffees/teas:	Fluid intake:	Totals:			

THURSDAY		kJ/Cal	Fat	Protein	Carbs
Breakfast Time: am/pm					
Lunch Time: am/pm					
Dinner Time: am/pm					
Snacks:					
Coffees/teas:	Fluid intake:	Totals:			

FRIDAY			kJ/Cal	Fat	Protein	Carbs
Breakfast Time: am/pm						
Lunch Time: am/pm						
Dinner Time: am/pm						
Snacks:						
Coffees/teas:	Fluid intake:	Totals:				

SATURDAY			kJ/Cal	Fat	Protein	Carbs
Breakfast Time: am/pm						
Lunch Time: am/pm						
Dinner Time: am/pm						
Snacks:						
Coffees/teas:	Fluid intake:	Totals:				

SUNDAY			kJ/Cal	Fat	Protein	Carbs
Breakfast Time: am/pm						
Lunch Time: am/pm						
Dinner Time: am/pm						
Snacks:						
Coffees/teas:	Fluid intake:	Totals:				

Units of alcohol this week: ☐ Total alcohol kJ/Cal: ☐

Vitamins and supplements

Weekly Totals	kJ/Cal	Fat	Protein	Carbs

Weekly Personal Summary

Energy level [1–5] ☐   Stress level [1–5] ☐

Hours of sleep ☐   Sleep quality [1–5] ☐

Mood [1–5] ☐   Appetite [1–5] ☐

kJ/Cal intake

Planned kJ/Cal	
Actual kJ/Cal	
Difference [+/-]	

Weight at start of week ☐
Weight at end of week ☐
BMI at start of week ☐
BMI at end of week ☐

Injuries or illnesses _____

Week Beginning

[   ] / [   ] /

Planned exercise sessions this week

	Exercise	Completed [Y/N]
Monday		
Tuesday		
Wednesday		
Thursday		
Friday		
Saturday		
Sunday		

Strength Training

MONDAY

Focus area	Equipment	SET 1		SET 2		SET 3		SET 4	
		Weight	Reps	Weight	Reps	Weight	Reps	Weight	Reps

TUESDAY

Focus area	Equipment	SET 1		SET 2		SET 3		SET 4	
		Weight	Reps	Weight	Reps	Weight	Reps	Weight	Reps

WEDNESDAY

Focus area	Equipment	SET 1		SET 2		SET 3		SET 4	
		Weight	Reps	Weight	Reps	Weight	Reps	Weight	Reps

THURSDAY

Focus area	Equipment	SET 1		SET 2		SET 3		SET 4	
		Weight	Reps	Weight	Reps	Weight	Reps	Weight	Reps

FRIDAY

Focus area	Equipment	SET 1		SET 2		SET 3		SET 4	
		Weight	Reps	Weight	Reps	Weight	Reps	Weight	Reps

SATURDAY

Focus area	Equipment	SET 1		SET 2		SET 3		SET 4	
		Weight	Reps	Weight	Reps	Weight	Reps	Weight	Reps

SUNDAY

Focus area	Equipment	SET 1		SET 2		SET 3		SET 4	
		Weight	Reps	Weight	Reps	Weight	Reps	Weight	Reps

Cardio Training

	Exercise	Time	Distance/resistance	Intensity	Heart rate	Ease	kJ/Cal expended
MONDAY							
							Total:

	Exercise	Time	Distance/resistance	Intensity	Heart rate	Ease	kJ/Cal expended
TUESDAY							
							Total:

	Exercise	Time	Distance/resistance	Intensity	Heart rate	Ease	kJ/Cal expended
WEDNESDAY							
							Total:

	Exercise	Time	Distance/resistance	Intensity	Heart rate	Ease	kJ/Cal expended
THURSDAY							
							Total:

	Exercise	Time	Distance/resistance	Intensity	Heart rate	Ease	kJ/Cal expended
FRIDAY							
							Total:

	Exercise	Time	Distance/resistance	Intensity	Heart rate	Ease	kJ/Cal expended
SATURDAY							
							Total:

	Exercise	Time	Distance/resistance	Intensity	Heart rate	Ease	kJ/Cal expended
SUNDAY							
							Total:

Weekly Total:

Food Diary

MONDAY		kJ/Cal	Fat	Protein	Carbs
Breakfast Time: am/pm					
Lunch Time: am/pm					
Dinner Time: am/pm					
Snacks:					
Coffees/teas:	**Fluid intake:** **Totals:**				

TUESDAY		kJ/Cal	Fat	Protein	Carbs
Breakfast Time: am/pm					
Lunch Time: am/pm					
Dinner Time: am/pm					
Snacks:					
Coffees/teas:	**Fluid intake:** **Totals:**				

WEDNESDAY		kJ/Cal	Fat	Protein	Carbs
Breakfast Time: am/pm					
Lunch Time: am/pm					
Dinner Time: am/pm					
Snacks:					
Coffees/teas:	**Fluid intake:** **Totals:**				

THURSDAY		kJ/Cal	Fat	Protein	Carbs
Breakfast Time: am/pm					
Lunch Time: am/pm					
Dinner Time: am/pm					
Snacks:					
Coffees/teas:	**Fluid intake:** **Totals:**				

FRIDAY		kJ/Cal	Fat	Protein	Carbs
Breakfast Time: am/pm					
Lunch Time: am/pm					
Dinner Time: am/pm					
Snacks:					
Coffees/teas:	Fluid intake:	Totals:			

SATURDAY		kJ/Cal	Fat	Protein	Carbs
Breakfast Time: am/pm					
Lunch Time: am/pm					
Dinner Time: am/pm					
Snacks:					
Coffees/teas:	Fluid intake:	Totals:			

SUNDAY		kJ/Cal	Fat	Protein	Carbs
Breakfast Time: am/pm					
Lunch Time: am/pm					
Dinner Time: am/pm					
Snacks:					
Coffees/teas:	Fluid intake:	Totals:			

Units of alcohol this week: [ ]   Total alcohol kJ/Cal: [ ]

Vitamins and supplements

	kJ/Cal	Fat	Protein	Carbs
Weekly Totals				

Weekly Personal Summary

Energy level [1–5]   Stress level [1–5]

Hours of sleep [ ]   Sleep quality [1–5]

Mood [1–5]   Appetite [1–5]

kJ/Cal intake

Planned kJ/Cal	
Actual kJ/Cal	
Difference [+/-]	

Weight at start of week [ ]

Weight at end of week [ ]

BMI at start of week [ ]

BMI at end of week [ ]

Injuries or illnesses [ ]

Monthly Summary

MONTH 1   DATE [/   /   ]   AGE [   ]   HEIGHT [   ]

Physical Measurements		
Last Mth's Target		This Mth's Result
	Weight	
	BMI	
	Waist–hip ratio	
	Chest, relaxed	
	Chest, expanded	
	Waist	
	Stomach	
	Hips	
	Neck	
	Shoulders	
	Right upper arm, relaxed	
	Right upper arm, flexed	
	Left upper arm, relaxed	
	Left upper arm, flexed	
	Right forearm, relaxed	
	Right forearm, flexed	
	Left forearm, relaxed	
	Left forearm, flexed	
	Right upper thigh	
	Right lower thigh	
	Left upper thigh	
	Left lower thigh	
	Right calf	
	Left calf	

Total your weekly results and divide by the number of weeks to get your average.

Average monthly mood — 1–5 [   ]

Average monthly appetite — 1–5 [   ]

Average monthly energy level — 1–5 [   ]

Average monthly stress level — 1–5 [   ]

Average weekly hours of sleep [   ]

Average monthly sleep quality — 1–5 [   ]

Number of planned exercise sessions this month [   ]

Number of completed exercise sessions this month [   ]

Average daily coffee/teas [   ]

Average daily fluid intake [   ]

Average weekly units of alcohol [   ]

Cardiovascular Fitness Test				
	Last Month	Target	Actual	Next Mth's Target
Resting heart rate				
Working heart rate: after 3 minutes				
after 6 minutes				
after 9 minutes				
Recovery heart rate: at course completion				
1 minute after completion				
2 minutes after completion				
3 minutes after completion				
Completion time				

Endurance				
	Last Month	Target	Actual	Next Mth's Target
Time to run 2km/1 mile				
Number of push-ups before you have to stop				
Number of sit-ups before you have to stop				
Number of squats before you have to stop				
Number of cm/inches you can stretch up to or beyond your feet (+/-)				
Time you can balance on one foot: right leg left leg				

Total your daily dietary results to get your monthly total.

Dietary Results			
	Target	Result	Difference [+/-]
Fat intake			
kj/Cal intake			
Carbs intake			
Protein intake			

Next Month's Targets

Physical Measurement Targets			
	Next Mth's Target		Next Mth's Target
Weight		Left upper arm, relaxed	
BMI		Left upper arm, flexed	
Waist–hip ratio		Right forearm, relaxed	
Chest, relaxed		Right forearm, flexed	
Chest, expanded		Left forearm, relaxed	
Waist		Left forearm, flexed	
Stomach		Right upper thigh	
Hips		Right lower thigh	
Neck		Left upper thigh	
Shoulders		Left lower thigh	
Right upper arm, relaxed		Right calf	
Right upper arm, flexed		Left calf	

Dietary Targets			
	Next Mth's Target		Next Mth's Target
Fat		Daily fluid intake	
kJ/Cal		Daily coffee/tea intake	
Protein		Weekly alcohol intake	
Carbs			

Monthly Summary

MONTH 2   **DATE** [/ /]   **AGE** [ ]   **HEIGHT** [ ]

Physical Measurements		
Last Mth's Target		**This Mth's Result**
	Weight	
	BMI	
	Waist–hip ratio	
	Chest, relaxed	
	Chest, expanded	
	Waist	
	Stomach	
	Hips	
	Neck	
	Shoulders	
	Right upper arm, relaxed	
	Right upper arm, flexed	
	Left upper arm, relaxed	
	Left upper arm, flexed	
	Right forearm, relaxed	
	Right forearm, flexed	
	Left forearm, relaxed	
	Left forearm, flexed	
	Right upper thigh	
	Right lower thigh	
	Left upper thigh	
	Left lower thigh	
	Right calf	
	Left calf	

Total your weekly results and divide by the number of weeks to get your average.

Average monthly mood [1–5]

Average monthly appetite [1–5]

Average monthly energy level [1–5]

Average monthly stress level [1–5]

Average weekly hours of sleep [ ]

Average monthly sleep quality [1–5]

Number of planned exercise sessions this month [ ]

Number of completed exercise sessions this month [ ]

Average daily coffee/teas [ ]

Average daily fluid intake [ ]

Average weekly units of alcohol [ ]

Cardiovascular Fitness Test				
	Last Month	**Target**	**Actual**	**Next Mth's Target**
Resting heart rate				
Working heart rate: after 3 minutes				
after 6 minutes				
after 9 minutes				
Recovery heart rate: at course completion				
1 minute after completion				
2 minutes after completion				
3 minutes after completion				
Completion time				

Endurance				
	Last Month	Target	Actual	Next Mth's Target
Time to run 2km/1 mile				
Number of push-ups before you have to stop				
Number of sit-ups before you have to stop				
Number of squats before you have to stop				
Number of cm/inches you can stretch up to or beyond your feet (+/-)				
Time you can balance on one foot: right leg left leg				

Total your daily dietary results to get your monthly total.

Dietary Results			
	Target	Result	Difference [+/-]
Fat intake			
kj/Cal intake			
Carbs intake			
Protein intake			

Next Month's Targets

Physical Measurement Targets			
	Next Mth's Target		Next Mth's Target
Weight		Left upper arm, relaxed	
BMI		Left upper arm, flexed	
Waist–hip ratio		Right forearm, relaxed	
Chest, relaxed		Right forearm, flexed	
Chest, expanded		Left forearm, relaxed	
Waist		Left forearm, flexed	
Stomach		Right upper thigh	
Hips		Right lower thigh	
Neck		Left upper thigh	
Shoulders		Left lower thigh	
Right upper arm, relaxed		Right calf	
Right upper arm, flexed		Left calf	

Dietary Targets			
	Next Mth's Target		Next Mth's Target
Fat		Daily fluid intake	
kJ/Cal		Daily coffee/tea intake	
Protein		Weekly alcohol intake	
Carbs			

Monthly Summary

MONTH 3   DATE [/ /]   AGE [   ]   HEIGHT [   ]

Physical Measurements		
Last Mth's Target		**This Mth's Result**
	Weight	
	BMI	
	Waist–hip ratio	
	Chest, relaxed	
	Chest, expanded	
	Waist	
	Stomach	
	Hips	
	Neck	
	Shoulders	
	Right upper arm, relaxed	
	Right upper arm, flexed	
	Left upper arm, relaxed	
	Left upper arm, flexed	
	Right forearm, relaxed	
	Right forearm, flexed	
	Left forearm, relaxed	
	Left forearm, flexed	
	Right upper thigh	
	Right lower thigh	
	Left upper thigh	
	Left lower thigh	
	Right calf	
	Left calf	

Total your weekly results and divide by the number of weeks to get your average.

Average monthly mood [1–5]

Average monthly appetite [1–5]

Average monthly energy level [1–5]

Average monthly stress level [1–5]

Average weekly hours of sleep [ ]

Average monthly sleep quality [1–5]

Number of planned exercise sessions this month [ ]

Number of completed exercise sessions this month [ ]

Average daily coffee/teas [ ]

Average daily fluid intake [ ]

Average weekly units of alcohol [ ]

Cardiovascular Fitness Test				
	Last Month	Target	Actual	Next Mth's Target
Resting heart rate				
Working heart rate: after 3 minutes				
after 6 minutes				
after 9 minutes				
Recovery heart rate: at course completion				
1 minute after completion				
2 minutes after completion				
3 minutes after completion				
Completion time				

Endurance				
	Last Month	Target	Actual	Next Mth's Target
Time to run 2km/1 mile				
Number of push-ups before you have to stop				
Number of sit-ups before you have to stop				
Number of squats before you have to stop				
Number of cm/inches you can stretch up to or beyond your feet (+/-)				
Time you can balance on one foot: right leg left leg				

Total your daily dietary results to get your monthly total.

Dietary Results			
	Target	Result	Difference [+/-]
Fat intake			
kj/Cal intake			
Carbs intake			
Protein intake			

Next Month's Targets

Physical Measurement Targets			
	Next Mth's Target		Next Mth's Target
Weight		Left upper arm, relaxed	
BMI		Left upper arm, flexed	
Waist–hip ratio		Right forearm, relaxed	
Chest, relaxed		Right forearm, flexed	
Chest, expanded		Left forearm, relaxed	
Waist		Left forearm, flexed	
Stomach		Right upper thigh	
Hips		Right lower thigh	
Neck		Left upper thigh	
Shoulders		Left lower thigh	
Right upper arm, relaxed		Right calf	
Right upper arm, flexed		Left calf	

Dietary Targets			
	Next Mth's Target		Next Mth's Target
Fat		Daily fluid intake	
kJ/Cal		Daily coffee/tea intake	
Protein		Weekly alcohol intake	
Carbs			

Monthly Summary

MONTH 4   **DATE** [/ /]   **AGE** [ ]   **HEIGHT** [ ]

Physical Measurements		
Last Mth's Target		This Mth's Result
	Weight	
	BMI	
	Waist–hip ratio	
	Chest, relaxed	
	Chest, expanded	
	Waist	
	Stomach	
	Hips	
	Neck	
	Shoulders	
	Right upper arm, relaxed	
	Right upper arm, flexed	
	Left upper arm, relaxed	
	Left upper arm, flexed	
	Right forearm, relaxed	
	Right forearm, flexed	
	Left forearm, relaxed	
	Left forearm, flexed	
	Right upper thigh	
	Right lower thigh	
	Left upper thigh	
	Left lower thigh	
	Right calf	
	Left calf	

Total your weekly results and divide by the number of weeks to get your average.

Average monthly mood   1–5 [ ]

Average monthly appetite   1–5 [ ]

Average monthly energy level   1–5 [ ]

Average monthly stress level   1–5 [ ]

Average weekly hours of sleep [ ]

Average monthly sleep quality   1–5 [ ]

Number of planned exercise sessions this month [ ]

Number of completed exercise sessions this month [ ]

Average daily coffee/teas [ ]

Average daily fluid intake [ ]

Average weekly units of alcohol [ ]

Cardiovascular Fitness Test				
	Last Month	Target	Actual	Next Mth's Target
Resting heart rate				
Working heart rate: after 3 minutes				
after 6 minutes				
after 9 minutes				
Recovery heart rate: at course completion				
1 minute after completion				
2 minutes after completion				
3 minutes after completion				
Completion time				

Endurance				
	Last Month	Target	Actual	Next Mth's Target
Time to run 2km/1 mile				
Number of push-ups before you have to stop				
Number of sit-ups before you have to stop				
Number of squats before you have to stop				
Number of cm/inches you can stretch up to or beyond your feet (+/-)				
Time you can balance on one foot: right leg / left leg				

Total your daily dietary results to get your monthly total.

Dietary Results			
	Target	Result	Difference [+/-]
Fat intake			
kj/Cal intake			
Carbs intake			
Protein intake			

Next Month's Targets

Physical Measurement Targets			
	Next Mth's Target		Next Mth's Target
Weight		Left upper arm, relaxed	
BMI		Left upper arm, flexed	
Waist–hip ratio		Right forearm, relaxed	
Chest, relaxed		Right forearm, flexed	
Chest, expanded		Left forearm, relaxed	
Waist		Left forearm, flexed	
Stomach		Right upper thigh	
Hips		Right lower thigh	
Neck		Left upper thigh	
Shoulders		Left lower thigh	
Right upper arm, relaxed		Right calf	
Right upper arm, flexed		Left calf	

Dietary Targets			
	Next Mth's Target		Next Mth's Target
Fat		Daily fluid intake	
kJ/Cal		Daily coffee/tea intake	
Protein		Weekly alcohol intake	
Carbs			

Monthly Summary

MONTH 5   DATE [/ /]   AGE [ ]   HEIGHT [ ]

Physical Measurements		
Last Mth's Target		**This Mth's Result**
	Weight	
	BMI	
	Waist–hip ratio	
	Chest, relaxed	
	Chest, expanded	
	Waist	
	Stomach	
	Hips	
	Neck	
	Shoulders	
	Right upper arm, relaxed	
	Right upper arm, flexed	
	Left upper arm, relaxed	
	Left upper arm, flexed	
	Right forearm, relaxed	
	Right forearm, flexed	
	Left forearm, relaxed	
	Left forearm, flexed	
	Right upper thigh	
	Right lower thigh	
	Left upper thigh	
	Left lower thigh	
	Right calf	
	Left calf	

Total your weekly results and divide by the number of weeks to get your average.

Average monthly mood [1–5]
Average monthly appetite [1–5]
Average monthly energy level [1–5]
Average monthly stress level [1–5]
Average weekly hours of sleep [ ]
Average monthly sleep quality [1–5]
Number of planned exercise sessions this month [ ]
Number of completed exercise sessions this month [ ]
Average daily coffee/teas [ ]
Average daily fluid intake [ ]
Average weekly units of alcohol [ ]

Cardiovascular Fitness Test				
	Last Month	**Target**	**Actual**	**Next Mth's Target**
Resting heart rate				
Working heart rate: after 3 minutes				
after 6 minutes				
after 9 minutes				
Recovery heart rate: at course completion				
1 minute after completion				
2 minutes after completion				
3 minutes after completion				
Completion time				

Endurance				
	Last Month	Target	Actual	Next Mth's Target
Time to run 2km/1 mile				
Number of push-ups before you have to stop				
Number of sit-ups before you have to stop				
Number of squats before you have to stop				
Number of cm/inches you can stretch up to or beyond your feet (+/-)				
Time you can balance on one foot: right leg left leg				

Total your daily dietary results to get your monthly total.

Dietary Results			
	Target	Result	Difference [+/-]
Fat intake			
kj/Cal intake			
Carbs intake			
Protein intake			

Next Month's Targets

Physical Measurement Targets			
	Next Mth's Target		Next Mth's Target
Weight		Left upper arm, relaxed	
BMI		Left upper arm, flexed	
Waist–hip ratio		Right forearm, relaxed	
Chest, relaxed		Right forearm, flexed	
Chest, expanded		Left forearm, relaxed	
Waist		Left forearm, flexed	
Stomach		Right upper thigh	
Hips		Right lower thigh	
Neck		Left upper thigh	
Shoulders		Left lower thigh	
Right upper arm, relaxed		Right calf	
Right upper arm, flexed		Left calf	

Dietary Targets			
	Next Mth's Target		Next Mth's Target
Fat		Daily fluid intake	
kJ/Cal		Daily coffee/tea intake	
Protein		Weekly alcohol intake	
Carbs			

Monthly Summary

MONTH 6 **DATE** [/ /] **AGE** [ ] **HEIGHT** [ ]

Physical Measurements		
Last Mth's Target		**This Mth's Result**
	Weight	
	BMI	
	Waist–hip ratio	
	Chest, relaxed	
	Chest, expanded	
	Waist	
	Stomach	
	Hips	
	Neck	
	Shoulders	
	Right upper arm, relaxed	
	Right upper arm, flexed	
	Left upper arm, relaxed	
	Left upper arm, flexed	
	Right forearm, relaxed	
	Right forearm, flexed	
	Left forearm, relaxed	
	Left forearm, flexed	
	Right upper thigh	
	Right lower thigh	
	Left upper thigh	
	Left lower thigh	
	Right calf	
	Left calf	

Total your weekly results and divide by the number of weeks to get your average.

Average monthly mood [ ] 1–5

Average monthly appetite [ ] 1–5

Average monthly energy level [ ] 1–5

Average monthly stress level [ ] 1–5

Average weekly hours of sleep [ ]

Average monthly sleep quality [ ] 1–5

Number of planned exercise sessions this month [ ]

Number of completed exercise sessions this month [ ]

Average daily coffee/teas [ ]

Average daily fluid intake [ ]

Average weekly units of alcohol [ ]

Cardiovascular Fitness Test				
	Last Month	**Target**	**Actual**	**Next Mth's Target**
Resting heart rate				
Working heart rate: after 3 minutes				
after 6 minutes				
after 9 minutes				
Recovery heart rate: at course completion				
1 minute after completion				
2 minutes after completion				
3 minutes after completion				
Completion time				

Endurance				
	Last Month	Target	Actual	Next Mth's Target
Time to run 2km/1 mile				
Number of push-ups before you have to stop				
Number of sit-ups before you have to stop				
Number of squats before you have to stop				
Number of cm/inches you can stretch up to or beyond your feet (+/-)				
Time you can balance on one foot: right leg left leg				

Total your daily dietary results to get your monthly total.

Dietary Results			
	Target	Result	Difference [+/-]
Fat intake			
kj/Cal intake			
Carbs intake			
Protein intake			

Next Month's Targets

Physical Measurement Targets			
	Next Mth's Target		Next Mth's Target
Weight		Left upper arm, relaxed	
BMI		Left upper arm, flexed	
Waist–hip ratio		Right forearm, relaxed	
Chest, relaxed		Right forearm, flexed	
Chest, expanded		Left forearm, relaxed	
Waist		Left forearm, flexed	
Stomach		Right upper thigh	
Hips		Right lower thigh	
Neck		Left upper thigh	
Shoulders		Left lower thigh	
Right upper arm, relaxed		Right calf	
Right upper arm, flexed		Left calf	

Dietary Targets			
	Next Mth's Target		Next Mth's Target
Fat		Daily fluid intake	
kJ/Cal		Daily coffee/tea intake	
Protein		Weekly alcohol intake	
Carbs			

Monthly Summary

MONTH 7 **DATE** [/ /] **AGE** [ ] **HEIGHT** [ ]

Physical Measurements		
Last Mth's Target		**This Mth's Result**
	Weight	
	BMI	
	Waist–hip ratio	
	Chest, relaxed	
	Chest, expanded	
	Waist	
	Stomach	
	Hips	
	Neck	
	Shoulders	
	Right upper arm, relaxed	
	Right upper arm, flexed	
	Left upper arm, relaxed	
	Left upper arm, flexed	
	Right forearm, relaxed	
	Right forearm, flexed	
	Left forearm, relaxed	
	Left forearm, flexed	
	Right upper thigh	
	Right lower thigh	
	Left upper thigh	
	Left lower thigh	
	Right calf	
	Left calf	

Total your weekly results and divide by the number of weeks to get your average.

Average monthly mood — 1–5 [ ]

Average monthly appetite — 1–5 [ ]

Average monthly energy level — 1–5 [ ]

Average monthly stress level — 1–5 [ ]

Average weekly hours of sleep [ ]

Average monthly sleep quality — 1–5 [ ]

Number of planned exercise sessions this month [ ]

Number of completed exercise sessions this month [ ]

Average daily coffee/teas [ ]

Average daily fluid intake [ ]

Average weekly units of alcohol [ ]

Cardiovascular Fitness Test				
	Last Month	**Target**	**Actual**	**Next Mth's Target**
Resting heart rate				
Working heart rate: after 3 minutes				
after 6 minutes				
after 9 minutes				
Recovery heart rate: at course completion				
1 minute after completion				
2 minutes after completion				
3 minutes after completion				
Completion time				

Endurance				
	Last Month	Target	Actual	Next Mth's Target
Time to run 2km/1 mile				
Number of push-ups before you have to stop				
Number of sit-ups before you have to stop				
Number of squats before you have to stop				
Number of cm/inches you can stretch up to or beyond your feet (+/-)				
Time you can balance on one foot: right leg left leg				

Total your daily dietary results to get your monthly total.

Dietary Results			
	Target	Result	Difference [+/-]
Fat intake			
kJ/Cal intake			
Carbs intake			
Protein intake			

Next Month's Targets

Physical Measurement Targets			
	Next Mth's Target		Next Mth's Target
Weight		Left upper arm, relaxed	
BMI		Left upper arm, flexed	
Waist–hip ratio		Right forearm, relaxed	
Chest, relaxed		Right forearm, flexed	
Chest, expanded		Left forearm, relaxed	
Waist		Left forearm, flexed	
Stomach		Right upper thigh	
Hips		Right lower thigh	
Neck		Left upper thigh	
Shoulders		Left lower thigh	
Right upper arm, relaxed		Right calf	
Right upper arm, flexed		Left calf	

Dietary Targets			
	Next Mth's Target		Next Mth's Target
Fat		Daily fluid intake	
kJ/Cal		Daily coffee/tea intake	
Protein		Weekly alcohol intake	
Carbs			

Monthly Summary

MONTH 8 DATE [/ /] AGE [ ] HEIGHT [ ]

Physical Measurements		
Last Mth's Target		This Mth's Result
	Weight	
	BMI	
	Waist–hip ratio	
	Chest, relaxed	
	Chest, expanded	
	Waist	
	Stomach	
	Hips	
	Neck	
	Shoulders	
	Right upper arm, relaxed	
	Right upper arm, flexed	
	Left upper arm, relaxed	
	Left upper arm, flexed	
	Right forearm, relaxed	
	Right forearm, flexed	
	Left forearm, relaxed	
	Left forearm, flexed	
	Right upper thigh	
	Right lower thigh	
	Left upper thigh	
	Left lower thigh	
	Right calf	
	Left calf	

Total your weekly results and divide by the number of weeks to get your average.

Average monthly mood 1–5 [ ]

Average monthly appetite 1–5 [ ]

Average monthly energy level 1–5 [ ]

Average monthly stress level 1–5 [ ]

Average weekly hours of sleep [ ]

Average monthly sleep quality 1–5 [ ]

Number of planned exercise sessions this month [ ]

Number of completed exercise sessions this month [ ]

Average daily coffee/ teas [ ]

Average daily fluid intake [ ]

Average weekly units of alcohol [ ]

Cardiovascular Fitness Test				
	Last Month	Target	Actual	Next Mth's Target
Resting heart rate				
Working heart rate: after 3 minutes				
after 6 minutes				
after 9 minutes				
Recovery heart rate: at course completion				
1 minute after completion				
2 minutes after completion				
3 minutes after completion				
Completion time				

Endurance				
	Last Month	Target	Actual	Next Mth's Target
Time to run 2km/1 mile				
Number of push-ups before you have to stop				
Number of sit-ups before you have to stop				
Number of squats before you have to stop				
Number of cm/inches you can stretch up to or beyond your feet (+/-)				
Time you can balance on one foot: right leg left leg				

Total your daily dietary results to get your monthly total.

Dietary Results			
	Target	Result	Difference [+/-]
Fat intake			
kj/Cal intake			
Carbs intake			
Protein intake			

Next Month's Targets

Physical Measurement Targets			
	Next Mth's Target		Next Mth's Target
Weight		Left upper arm, relaxed	
BMI		Left upper arm, flexed	
Waist–hip ratio		Right forearm, relaxed	
Chest, relaxed		Right forearm, flexed	
Chest, expanded		Left forearm, relaxed	
Waist		Left forearm, flexed	
Stomach		Right upper thigh	
Hips		Right lower thigh	
Neck		Left upper thigh	
Shoulders		Left lower thigh	
Right upper arm, relaxed		Right calf	
Right upper arm, flexed		Left calf	

Dietary Targets			
	Next Mth's Target		Next Mth's Target
Fat		Daily fluid intake	
kJ/Cal		Daily coffee/tea intake	
Protein		Weekly alcohol intake	
Carbs			

Monthly Summary

MONTH 9 DATE [/   /   ] AGE [   ] HEIGHT [   ]

Physical Measurements		
Last Mth's Target		**This Mth's Result**
	Weight	
	BMI	
	Waist–hip ratio	
	Chest, relaxed	
	Chest, expanded	
	Waist	
	Stomach	
	Hips	
	Neck	
	Shoulders	
	Right upper arm, relaxed	
	Right upper arm, flexed	
	Left upper arm, relaxed	
	Left upper arm, flexed	
	Right forearm, relaxed	
	Right forearm, flexed	
	Left forearm, relaxed	
	Left forearm, flexed	
	Right upper thigh	
	Right lower thigh	
	Left upper thigh	
	Left lower thigh	
	Right calf	
	Left calf	

Total your weekly results and divide by the number of weeks to get your average.

Average monthly mood — 1–5 [   ]

Average monthly appetite — 1–5 [   ]

Average monthly energy level — 1–5 [   ]

Average monthly stress level — 1–5 [   ]

Average weekly hours of sleep [   ]

Average monthly sleep quality — 1–5 [   ]

Number of planned exercise sessions this month [   ]

Number of completed exercise sessions this month [   ]

Average daily coffee/teas [   ]

Average daily fluid intake [   ]

Average weekly units of alcohol [   ]

Cardiovascular Fitness Test				
	Last Month	**Target**	**Actual**	**Next Mth's Target**
Resting heart rate				
Working heart rate: after 3 minutes				
after 6 minutes				
after 9 minutes				
Recovery heart rate: at course completion				
1 minute after completion				
2 minutes after completion				
3 minutes after completion				
Completion time				

Endurance

	Last Month	Target	Actual	Next Mth's Target
Time to run 2km/1 mile				
Number of push-ups before you have to stop				
Number of sit-ups before you have to stop				
Number of squats before you have to stop				
Number of cm/inches you can stretch up to or beyond your feet (+/-)				
Time you can balance on one foot: right leg left leg				

Total your daily dietary results to get your monthly total.

Dietary Results

	Target	Result	Difference [+/-]
Fat intake			
kj/Cal intake			
Carbs intake			
Protein intake			

Next Month's Targets

Physical Measurement Targets

	Next Mth's Target		Next Mth's Target
Weight		Left upper arm, relaxed	
BMI		Left upper arm, flexed	
Waist–hip ratio		Right forearm, relaxed	
Chest, relaxed		Right forearm, flexed	
Chest, expanded		Left forearm, relaxed	
Waist		Left forearm, flexed	
Stomach		Right upper thigh	
Hips		Right lower thigh	
Neck		Left upper thigh	
Shoulders		Left lower thigh	
Right upper arm, relaxed		Right calf	
Right upper arm, flexed		Left calf	

Dietary Targets

	Next Mth's Target		Next Mth's Target
Fat		Daily fluid intake	
kJ/Cal		Daily coffee/tea intake	
Protein		Weekly alcohol intake	
Carbs			

Monthly Summary

MONTH 10 **DATE** [/ /] **AGE** [ ] **HEIGHT** [ ]

Physical Measurements		
Last Mth's Target		**This Mth's Result**
	Weight	
	BMI	
	Waist–hip ratio	
	Chest, relaxed	
	Chest, expanded	
	Waist	
	Stomach	
	Hips	
	Neck	
	Shoulders	
	Right upper arm, relaxed	
	Right upper arm, flexed	
	Left upper arm, relaxed	
	Left upper arm, flexed	
	Right forearm, relaxed	
	Right forearm, flexed	
	Left forearm, relaxed	
	Left forearm, flexed	
	Right upper thigh	
	Right lower thigh	
	Left upper thigh	
	Left lower thigh	
	Right calf	
	Left calf	

Total your weekly results and divide by the number of weeks to get your average.

Average monthly mood	1–5 [ ]
Average monthly appetite	1–5 [ ]
Average monthly energy level	1–5 [ ]
Average monthly stress level	1–5 [ ]
Average weekly hours of sleep	[ ]
Average monthly sleep quality	1–5 [ ]
Number of planned exercise sessions this month	[ ]
Number of completed exercise sessions this month	[ ]
Average daily coffee/teas	[ ]
Average daily fluid intake	[ ]
Average weekly units of alcohol	[ ]

Cardiovascular Fitness Test				
	Last Month	**Target**	**Actual**	**Next Mth's Target**
Resting heart rate				
Working heart rate: after 3 minutes				
after 6 minutes				
after 9 minutes				
Recovery heart rate: at course completion				
1 minute after completion				
2 minutes after completion				
3 minutes after completion				
Completion time				

Endurance				
	Last Month	Target	Actual	Next Mth's Target
Time to run 2km/1 mile				
Number of push-ups before you have to stop				
Number of sit-ups before you have to stop				
Number of squats before you have to stop				
Number of cm/inches you can stretch up to or beyond your feet (+/-)				
Time you can balance on one foot: right leg left leg				

Total your daily dietary results to get your monthly total.

Dietary Results			
	Target	Result	Difference [+/-]
Fat intake			
kj/Cal intake			
Carbs intake			
Protein intake			

Next Month's Targets

Physical Measurement Targets			
	Next Mth's Target		Next Mth's Target
Weight		Left upper arm, relaxed	
BMI		Left upper arm, flexed	
Waist–hip ratio		Right forearm, relaxed	
Chest, relaxed		Right forearm, flexed	
Chest, expanded		Left forearm, relaxed	
Waist		Left forearm, flexed	
Stomach		Right upper thigh	
Hips		Right lower thigh	
Neck		Left upper thigh	
Shoulders		Left lower thigh	
Right upper arm, relaxed		Right calf	
Right upper arm, flexed		Left calf	

Dietary Targets			
	Next Mth's Target		Next Mth's Target
Fat		Daily fluid intake	
kJ/Cal		Daily coffee/tea intake	
Protein		Weekly alcohol intake	
Carbs			

Monthly Summary

MONTH 11　DATE [/ /]　AGE [ ]　HEIGHT [ ]

Physical Measurements		
Last Mth's Target		This Mth's Result
	Weight	
	BMI	
	Waist–hip ratio	
	Chest, relaxed	
	Chest, expanded	
	Waist	
	Stomach	
	Hips	
	Neck	
	Shoulders	
	Right upper arm, relaxed	
	Right upper arm, flexed	
	Left upper arm, relaxed	
	Left upper arm, flexed	
	Right forearm, relaxed	
	Right forearm, flexed	
	Left forearm, relaxed	
	Left forearm, flexed	
	Right upper thigh	
	Right lower thigh	
	Left upper thigh	
	Left lower thigh	
	Right calf	
	Left calf	

Total your weekly results and divide by the number of weeks to get your average.

Average monthly mood　1–5 [ ]

Average monthly appetite　1–5 [ ]

Average monthly energy level　1–5 [ ]

Average monthly stress level　1–5 [ ]

Average weekly hours of sleep [ ]

Average monthly sleep quality　1–5 [ ]

Number of planned exercise sessions this month [ ]

Number of completed exercise sessions this month [ ]

Average daily coffee/teas [ ]

Average daily fluid intake [ ]

Average weekly units of alcohol [ ]

Cardiovascular Fitness Test				
	Last Month	Target	Actual	Next Mth's Target
Resting heart rate				
Working heart rate: after 3 minutes				
after 6 minutes				
after 9 minutes				
Recovery heart rate: at course completion				
1 minute after completion				
2 minutes after completion				
3 minutes after completion				
Completion time				

Endurance				
	Last Month	Target	Actual	Next Mth's Target
Time to run 2km/1 mile				
Number of push-ups before you have to stop				
Number of sit-ups before you have to stop				
Number of squats before you have to stop				
Number of cm/inches you can stretch up to or beyond your feet (+/-)				
Time you can balance on one foot: right leg left leg				

Total your daily dietary results to get your monthly total.

Dietary Results			
	Target	Result	Difference [+/-]
Fat intake			
kJ/Cal intake			
Carbs intake			
Protein intake			

Next Month's Targets

Physical Measurement Targets			
	Next Mth's Target		Next Mth's Target
Weight		Left upper arm, relaxed	
BMI		Left upper arm, flexed	
Waist–hip ratio		Right forearm, relaxed	
Chest, relaxed		Right forearm, flexed	
Chest, expanded		Left forearm, relaxed	
Waist		Left forearm, flexed	
Stomach		Right upper thigh	
Hips		Right lower thigh	
Neck		Left upper thigh	
Shoulders		Left lower thigh	
Right upper arm, relaxed		Right calf	
Right upper arm, flexed		Left calf	

Dietary Targets			
	Next Mth's Target		Next Mth's Target
Fat		Daily fluid intake	
kJ/Cal		Daily coffee/tea intake	
Protein		Weekly alcohol intake	
Carbs			

Monthly Summary

MONTH 12 **DATE** [/ /] **AGE** [ ] **HEIGHT** [ ]

Physical Measurements	
Last Mth's Target	**This Mth's Result**
	Weight	
	BMI	
	Waist–hip ratio	
	Chest, relaxed	
	Chest, expanded	
	Waist	
	Stomach	
	Hips	
	Neck	
	Shoulders	
	Right upper arm, relaxed	
	Right upper arm, flexed	
	Left upper arm, relaxed	
	Left upper arm, flexed	
	Right forearm, relaxed	
	Right forearm, flexed	
	Left forearm, relaxed	
	Left forearm, flexed	
	Right upper thigh	
	Right lower thigh	
	Left upper thigh	
	Left lower thigh	
	Right calf	
	Left calf	

Total your weekly results and divide by the number of weeks to get your average.

Average monthly mood — 1–5 [ ]

Average monthly appetite — 1–5 [ ]

Average monthly energy level — 1–5 [ ]

Average monthly stress level — 1–5 [ ]

Average weekly hours of sleep [ ]

Average monthly sleep quality — 1–5 [ ]

Number of planned exercise sessions this month [ ]

Number of completed exercise sessions this month [ ]

Average daily coffee/teas [ ]

Average daily fluid intake [ ]

Average weekly units of alcohol [ ]

Cardiovascular Fitness Test				
	Last Month	**Target**	**Actual**	**Next Mth's Target**
Resting heart rate				
Working heart rate: after 3 minutes				
after 6 minutes				
after 9 minutes				
Recovery heart rate: at course completion				
1 minute after completion				
2 minutes after completion				
3 minutes after completion				
Completion time				

Endurance				
	Last Month	Target	Actual	Next Mth's Target
Time to run 2km/1 mile				
Number of push-ups before you have to stop				
Number of sit-ups before you have to stop				
Number of squats before you have to stop				
Number of cm/inches you can stretch up to or beyond your feet (+/-)				
Time you can balance on one foot: right leg / left leg				

Total your daily dietary results to get your monthly total.

Dietary Results			
	Target	Result	Difference [+/-]
Fat intake			
kj/Cal intake			
Carbs intake			
Protein intake			

Next Month's Targets

Physical Measurement Targets			
	Next Mth's Target		Next Mth's Target
Weight		Left upper arm, relaxed	
BMI		Left upper arm, flexed	
Waist–hip ratio		Right forearm, relaxed	
Chest, relaxed		Right forearm, flexed	
Chest, expanded		Left forearm, relaxed	
Waist		Left forearm, flexed	
Stomach		Right upper thigh	
Hips		Right lower thigh	
Neck		Left upper thigh	
Shoulders		Left lower thigh	
Right upper arm, relaxed		Right calf	
Right upper arm, flexed		Left calf	

Dietary Targets			
	Next Mth's Target		Next Mth's Target
Fat		Daily fluid intake	
kJ/Cal		Daily coffee/tea intake	
Protein		Weekly alcohol intake	
Carbs			

End-of-Year Assessment

DATE [/ /]   AGE [ ]   HEIGHT [ ]

Physical Measurement Targets		Actual Physical Measurement Results		Difference [+/-]
Weight		Weight		
BMI		BMI		
Waist–hip ratio		Waist–hip ratio		
Chest, relaxed		Chest, relaxed		
Chest, expanded		Chest, expanded		
Waist		Waist		
Stomach		Stomach		
Hips		Hips		
Neck		Neck		
Shoulders		Shoulders		
Right upper arm, relaxed		Right upper arm, relaxed		
Right upper arm, flexed		Right upper arm, flexed		
Left upper arm, relaxed		Left upper arm, relaxed		
Left upper arm, flexed		Left upper arm, flexed		
Right forearm, relaxed		Right forearm, relaxed		
Right forearm, flexed		Right forearm, flexed		
Left forearm, relaxed		Left forearm, relaxed		
Left forearm, flexed		Left forearm, flexed		
Right upper thigh		Right upper thigh		
Right lower thigh		Right lower thigh		
Left upper thigh		Left upper thigh		
Left lower thigh		Left lower thigh		
Right calf		Right calf		
Left calf		Left calf		

Time how long it takes to run 2km/1 mile.	Target		Actual		Difference
Count how many push-ups you can do before you have to stop.	Target		Actual		Difference
Count how many sit-ups you can do before you have to stop.	Target		Actual		Difference
Count how many squats you can do before you have to stop.	Target		Actual		Difference
Sit with legs out straight. Place a ruler on the floor with the center between your feet. Record how many cm/inches you stretch up to or beyond your feet.	Target distance [+/-]		Actual distance [+/-]		Difference [+/-]
Time you can balance on one foot: right leg / left leg	Target		Actual		Difference

Cardiovascular Fitness Test			
	Start of Year Target Time	Actual	Difference [+/-]
Resting heart rate			
Working heart rate: after 3 minutes			
after 6 minutes			
after 9 minutes			
Recovery heart rate: at course completion			
1 minute after completion			
2 minutes after completion			
3 minutes after completion			
Completion time			

Current Personal Summary

Strength level — 1–5

Endurance level — 1–5

Satisfaction with fitness — 1–5

Satisfaction with weight — 1–5

Quality of diet — 1–5

Energy level — 1–5

Sleep quality — 1–5

Stress level — 1–5

Mood level — 1–5

End-of-Year Personal Summary

Yearly Heart Rate Graph

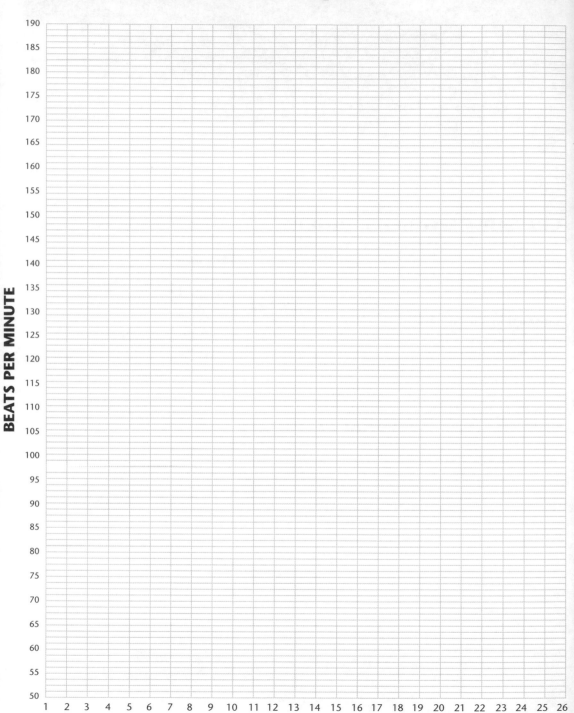

BEATS PER MINUTE

WEEK

Record your average weekly resting and maximum heart rates and graph your progress throughout the year.

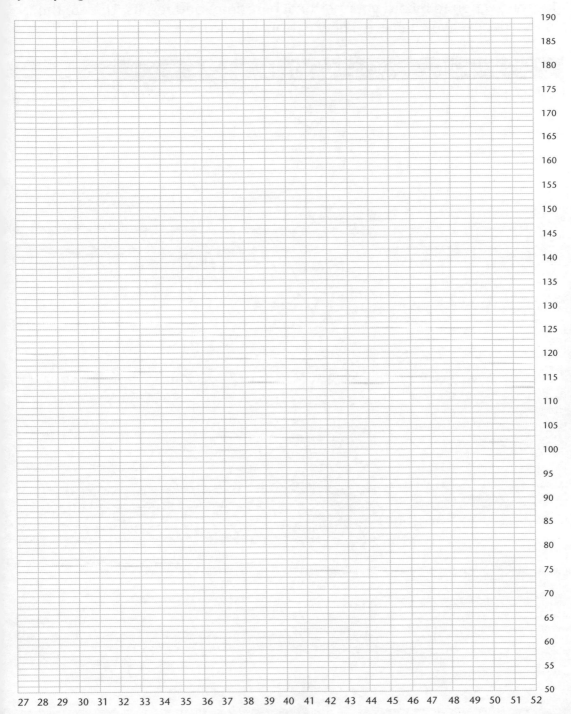

WEEK

BEATS PER MINUTE

Personal Bests

Use this section to record your personal best times and results. Update the chart whenever you achieve a new personal record.

EXERCISE	DATE	RECORD

EXERCISE	DATE	RECORD

Diet and Exercise Notes